Glencoe McGraw-Hill

Math Connects
Course 1

Chapter 3
Resource Masters

Glencoe

Consumable Workbooks Many of the worksheets contained in the Chapter Resource Masters are available as consumable workbooks in both English and Spanish.

	MHID	ISBN
Study Guide and Intervention Workbook	0-07-881032-9	978-0-07-881032-9
Skills Practice Workbook	0-07-881031-0	978-0-07-881031-2
Practice Workbook	0-07-881034-5	978-0-07-881034-3
Word Problem Practice Workbook	0-07-881033-7	978-0-07-881033-6

Spanish Versions

	MHID	ISBN
Study Guide and Intervention Workbook	0-07-881036-1	978-0-07-881036-7
Skills Practice Workbook	0-07-881035-3	978-0-07-881035-0
Practice Workbook	0-07-881038-8	978-0-07-881038-1
Word Problem Practice Workbook	0-07-881037-X	978-0-07-881037-4

Answers for Workbooks The answers for Chapter 3 of these workbooks can be found in the back of this Chapter Resource Masters booklet.

StudentWorks Plus™ This CD-ROM includes the entire Student Edition test along with the English workbooks listed above.

TeacherWorks Plus™ All of the materials found in this booklet are included for viewing, printing, and editing in this CD-ROM.

Spanish Assessment Masters (MHID: 0-07-881039-6, ISBN: 978-0-07-881039-8) These masters contain a Spanish version of Chapter 3 Test Form 2A and Form 2C.

 Glencoe

The McGraw-Hill Companies

Send all inquiries to:
Glencoe/McGraw-Hill
8787 Orion Place
Columbus, OH 43240

ISBN: 978-0-07-881021-3
MHID: 0-07-881021-3

Printed in the United States of America
4 5 6 7 8 9 10 REL 16 15 14 13 12 11 10

Math Connects, Course 1

CONTENTS

CONTENTS *(continued)*

Lesson 3-10
Problem-Solving Investigation: Reasonable Answers

Chapter 3 Assessment

Teacher's Guide to Using the
Chapter 3 Resource Masters

The *Chapter 3 Resource Masters* includes the core materials needed for Chapter 3. These materials include worksheets, extensions, and assessment options. The answers for these pages appear at the back of this booklet.

All of the materials found in this booklet are included for viewing and printing on the *TeacherWorks Plus*™ CD-ROM.

Chapter Resources

Student-Built Glossary (pages 1–2) These masters are a student study tool that presents up to twenty of the key vocabulary terms from the chapter. Students are to record definitions and/or examples for each term. You may suggest that students highlight or star the terms with which they are not familiar. Give this to students before beginning Lesson 3-1. Encourage them to add these pages to their mathematics study notebooks. Remind them to complete the appropriate words as they study each lesson.

Family Letter and Family Activity (pages 3–6) The letter informs your students' families of the mathematics they will be learning in this chapter. The family activity helps them to practice problems that are similar to those on the state test. A full solution for each problem is included. Spanish versions of these pages are also included. Give these to students to take home before beginning the chapter.

Anticipation Guide (pages 7–8) This master, presented in both English and Spanish, is a survey used before beginning the chapter to pinpoint what students may or may not know about the concepts in the chapter. Students will revisit this survey after they complete the chapter to see if their perceptions have changed.

Lesson Resources

Lesson Reading Guide Get Ready for the Lesson reiterates the questions from the beginning of the Student Edition lesson. Read the Lesson asks students to interpret the context of and relationships among terms in the lesson. Finally, Remember What You Learned asks students to summarize what they have learned using various representation techniques. Use as a study tool for note taking or as an informal reading assignment. It is also a helpful tool for ELL (English Language Learners).

Study Guide and Intervention This master provides vocabulary, key concepts, additional worked-out examples and Check Your Progress exercises to use as a reteaching activity. It can also be used in conjunction with the Student Edition as an instructional tool for students who have been absent.

Skills Practice This master focuses more on the computational nature of the lesson. Use as an additional practice option or as homework for second-day teaching of the lesson.

Practice This master closely follows the types of problems found in the Exercises section of the Student Edition and includes word problems. Use as an additional practice option or as homework for second-day teaching of the lesson.

Word Problem Practice This master includes additional practice in solving word problems that apply the concepts of the lesson. Use as an additional practice or as homework for second-day teaching of the lesson.

Enrichment These activities may extend the concepts of the lesson, offer a historical or multicultural look at the concepts, or widen students' perspectives on the mathematics they are learning. They are written for use with all levels of students.

Graphing Calculator, Scientific Calculator, or Spreadsheet Activities These activities present ways in which technology can be used with the concepts in some lessons of this chapter. Use as an alternative approach to some concepts or as an integral part of your lesson presentation.

Assessment Options

The assessment masters in the *Chapter 3 Resource Masters* offer a wide range of assessment tools for formative (monitoring) assessment and summative (final) assessment.

Student Recording Sheet This master corresponds with the Test Practice at the end of the chapter.

Extended-Response Rubric This master provides information for teachers and students on how to assess performance on open-ended questions.

Quizzes Four free-response quizzes offer assessment at appropriate intervals in the chapter.

Mid-Chapter Test This 1-page test provides an option to assess the first half of the chapter. It parallels the timing of the Mid-Chapter Quiz in the Student Edition and includes both multiple-choice and free-response questions.

Vocabulary Test This test is suitable for all students. It includes a list of vocabulary words and 10 questions to assess students' knowledge of those words. This can also be used in conjunction with one of the leveled chapter tests.

Leveled Chapter Tests

- *Form 1* contains multiple-choice questions and is intended for use with below grade level students.

- *Forms 2A and 2B* contain multiple-choice questions aimed at on grade level students. These tests are similar in format to offer comparable testing situations.

- *Forms 2C and 2D* contain free-response questions aimed at on grade level students. These tests are similar in format to offer comparable testing situations.

- *Form 3* is a free-response test for use with above grade level students.

All of the above mentioned tests include a free-response Bonus question.

Extended-Response Test Performance assessment tasks are suitable for all students. Samples answers and a scoring rubric are included for evaluation.

Standardized Test Practice These three pages are cumulative in nature. It includes two parts: multiple-choice questions with bubble-in answer format and short-answer free-response questions.

Answers

- The answers for the Anticipation Guide and Lesson Resources are provided as reduced pages with answers appearing in red.

- Full-size answer keys are provided for the assessment masters.

3 Student-Built Glossary

This is an alphabetical list of new vocabulary terms you will learn in Chapter 3. As you study the chapter, complete each term's definition or description. Remember to add the page number where you found the term. Add this page to your math study notebook to review vocabulary at the end of the chapter.

Vocabulary Term	Found on Page	Definition/Description/Example
clustering		
decimal inequality		
equivalent [ih-KWIHV-uh-luhnt] decimals		
expanded form		
front-end estimation		
standard form		

1

3 | **Family Letter**

Dear Parent or Guardian:

Decimals are all around us. They are on our bills, on our car odometer, and on our calculators. Understanding decimals and how to work with them is not only useful but important in today's world.

In **Chapter 3, Operations with Decimals**, your child will learn all about decimals—representing them, comparing them, ordering them, rounding them, adding them, subtracting them, estimating their sums and differences, and multiplying them. In the study of this chapter, your child will complete a variety of daily classroom assignments and activities and possibly produce a chapter project.

By signing this letter and returning it with your child, you agree to encourage your child by getting involved. Enclosed is an activity you can do with your child that practices how the math we will be learning in Chapter 3 might be tested. You may also wish to log on to **glencoe.com** for self-check quizzes and other study help. If you have any questions or comments, feel free to contact me at school.

Sincerely,

Signature of Parent or Guardian _____ Date _____

3 Family Activity

State Test Practice

Fold the page along the dashed line. Work each problem on another piece of paper. Then unfold the page to check your work.

1. Amber weighed three bags all containing different things. If Amber puts all three bags into a previously empty box, how much will the contents of the box weigh altogether?

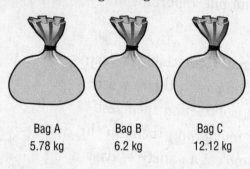

Bag A	Bag B	Bag C
5.78 kg	6.2 kg	12.12 kg

A 24.1 kg

B 18.52 kg

C 24.11 kg

D 23.92 kg

2. The following illustration shows the town of Big Pony, Montana. If Eddie rides his bike from French Street to English Avenue, how much farther does he ride than his sister, who rides her bike from French Street to Spanish Circle?

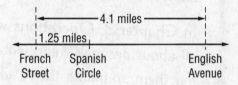

A 3.85 miles

B 2.85 miles

C 1.85 miles

D 3.15 miles

Fold here.

- -

Solution

1. *Hint: Remember to line up the decimals points when you add and subtract decimals!*

$$
\begin{array}{r}
\overset{1\ \ 1}{5.78} \\
6.20 \quad \leftarrow \text{Insert a zero to} \\
+\ 12.12 \quad \text{help you add} \\
\hline
24.10
\end{array}
$$

24.10 kg is equivalent to 24.1 kg.

Solution

2. *Hint: Remember to add zeros to the minuend (the number being subtracted from) if necessary to complete the subtraction problem. Also remember to borrow from the next greater place value when subtracting a larger number from a smaller number.*

$$
\begin{array}{r}
\overset{3\ \ 1010}{4.10} \quad \leftarrow \text{Insert a zero to} \\
-\ 1.25 \quad \text{help you subtract} \\
\hline
2.85
\end{array}
$$

The answer is **A.**

The answer is **B.**

3 ## Carta a la familia

Estimado padre o apoderado:

Los decimales nos rodean por todos lados. Los vemos en billetes, en el odómetro del carro y en las calculadoras. El entender los decimales y cómo trabajar con ellos, no es sólo importante sino también útil hoy en día.

En el **Capítulo 3, Operaciones con Decimales**, su hijo(a) aprenderá sobre decimales: cómo representarlos, compararlos, ordenarlos, redondearlos, sumarlos, restarlos y a estimar sus sumas y diferencias, y multiplicarlos. En el estudio de este capítulo, su hijo(a) completará una variedad de tareas y actividades diarias y es posible que trabaje en un proyecto del capítulo.

Al firmar esta carta y devolverla con su hijo(a), usted se compromete a ayudarlo(a) a participar en su aprendizaje. Junto con esta carta, va incluida una actividad que puede realizar con él(ella) y la cual practica lo que podrían encontrar en las pruebas de los conceptos matemáticos que aprenderán en el Capítulo 3. Además, visiten **glencoe.com** para ver autocontroles y otras ayudas para el estudio. Si tiene cualquier pregunta o comentario, por favor contácteme en la escuela.

Cordialmente,

Firma del padre o apoderado _____ Fecha _____

3 Actividad en familia

Práctica para la prueba estatal

Doblen la página a lo largo de las líneas punteadas. Resuelvan cada problema en otra hoja de papel. Luego, desdoblen la página y revisen las respuestas.

1. Amber pesó tres bolsas que contienen diferentes cosas. Si Amber coloca las tres bolsas en una caja que estaba vacía, ¿cuánto pesará todo el contenido de la caja?

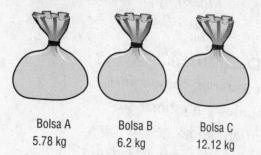

Bolsa A	Bolsa B	Bolsa C
5.78 kg	6.2 kg	12.12 kg

A 24.1 kg

B 18.52 kg

C 24.11 kg

D 23.92 kg

2. La siguiente ilustración muestra el pueblo Big Pony, en Montana. Si Eddie conduce su bicicleta de la calle Francia a la avenida Inglesa, ¿qué mayor distancia maneja él su bicicleta que su hermana, quien conduce su bicicleta de la calle Francia al círculo de España?

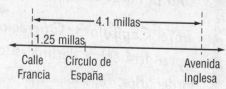

A 3.85 millas

B 2.85 millas

C 1.85 millas

D 3.15 millas

Doblen aquí.

Solución

1. *Ayuda: Recuerden alinear los puntos decimales al sumar y restar decimales.*

$$\begin{array}{r} \overset{1}{}\overset{1}{5}.78 \\ 6.20 \leftarrow \\ +\ 12.12 \\ \hline \end{array}$$ ← Agreguen un cero para facilitar la adición

24.10 kg equivalen a 24.1 kg.

Solución

2. *Ayuda: Recuerden añadir ceros al minuendo (el número del cual se resta), de ser necesario, para completar el problema de sustracción. También recuerden prestar del próximo valor de posición mayor al restar un número mayor de uno menor.*

$$\begin{array}{r} \overset{3}{4}.\overset{10}{1}\overset{10}{0} \\ -\ 1.25 \leftarrow \\ \hline 2.85 \end{array}$$ ← Agreguen un cero para facilitar la sustracción

La respuesta es **A.**

La respuesta es **B.**

3 Anticipation Guide

Adding and Subtracting Decimals

STEP 1 *Before you begin Chapter 3*

- Read each statement.
- Decide whether you Agree (A) or Disagree (D) with the statement.
- Write A or D in the first column OR if you are not sure whether you agree or disagree, write NS (Not Sure).

STEP 1 A, D, or NS	Statement	STEP 2 A or D
	1. The decimal 0.42 represents 42 hundredths.	
	2. 0.70 is greater than 0.7 because 70 is greater than 7.	
	3. On a number line, numbers to the right of zero are positive and numbers to the left of zero are negative.	
	4. To round a decimal to the hundredths place, look at the digit in the thousandths place.	
	5. The decimal 2.628 can be rounded to 2.63 or 2.6.	
	6. To estimate the sum of two decimals, always round both decimals to the tenths place.	
	7. Only decimals to the same place value can be added or subtracted.	
	8. When solving math problems, estimation can be used when an exact answer is not necessary.	
	9. To multiply a decimal by a whole number, you must first rewrite the whole number as a decimal.	
	10. The solution to 3.5×4.62 will have three decimal places.	
	11. Before dividing by a decimal, change the divisor to a whole number.	

STEP 2 *After you complete Chapter 3*

- Reread each statement and complete the last column by entering an A (Agree) or a D (Disagree).
- Did any of your opinions about the statements change from the first column?
- For those statements that you mark with a D, use a separate sheet of paper to explain why you disagree. Use examples, if possible.

3 Ejercicios preparatorios

Suma y resta decimales

Copyright © Glencoe/McGraw-Hill, a division of The McGraw-Hill Companies, Inc.

PASO 1 *Antes de comenzar el Capítulo 3*

- Lee cada enunciado.

- Decide si estás de acuerdo (A) o en desacuerdo (D) con el enunciado.

- Escribe A o D en la primera columna O si no estás seguro(a) de la respuesta, escribe NS (No estoy seguro(a).

PASO 1 A, D o NS	Enunciado	PASO 2 A o D
	1. El decimal 0.42 representa 42 centésimas.	
	2. 0.70 es mayor que 0.7 porque 70 es mayor que 7.	
	3. En una recta numérica, los números a la derecha de cero son positivos y los números a la izquierda de cero son negativos.	
	4. Para redondear un decimal al lugar de las centésimas, mira el dígito en el lugar de las milésimas.	
	5. El decimal 2.628 puede redondearse a 2.63 ó 2.6.	
	6. Para estimar la suma de dos decimales, redondea siempre los dos decimales al lugar de las décimas.	
	7. Sólo se pueden sumar o restar los decimales al mismo valor de posición.	
	8. Al resolver problemas matemáticos, se puede usar la estimacion cuando no se requiere una respuesta exacta.	
	9. Para multiplicar un decimal por un número entero, debes primero convertir el número entero en decimal.	
	10. La solución de 3.5×4.62 tendrá tres números decimales.	
	11. Antes de dividir entre un decimal, cambia el divisor por un número entero.	

PASO 2 *Después de completar el Capítulo 3*

- Vuelve a leer cada enunciado y completa la última columna con una A (acuerdo) o una D (desacuerdo).

- ¿Cambió cualquiera de tus opiniones sobre los enunciados de la primera columna?

- En una hoja de papel aparte, escribe ejemplos de por qué estás en desacuerdo con los enunciados que marcaste con una D.

3-1 **Lesson Reading Guide**

Representing Decimals

Get Ready for the Lesson

Complete the Mini Lab at the top of page 138 in your textbook.

Model each decimal using a place-value chart, money, a decimal model, and base-ten blocks.

1. 1.56

2. 0.85

3. 0.08

4. $2.25

Read the Lesson

5. What does the decimal point do?

6. How does changing the decimal point in 5.78 to 57.8 affect the value of the decimal?

Remember What You Learned

7. Look up the words *dime* and *decimal* in a dictionary. How is *dime* related to *decimal*? Explain how our money system (dollars, dimes, pennies) and the place-value chart use base ten.

Lesson 3–1

3-1 Study Guide and Intervention

Representing Decimals

Decimals can be written in standard form and expanded form.

Standard form is the usual way to write a decimal, such as 3.52. **Expanded form** is a sum of the products of each digit and its place, such as $(3 \times 1) + (5 \times 0.1) + (2 \times 0.01)$.

Example 1 Write 128.0732 in word form.

Place-Value Chart							
thousands	hundreds	tens	ones	tenths	hundredths	thousandths	ten-thousandths
0	1	2	8	0	7	3	2

In words, 128.0732 is *one hundred twenty-eight and seven hundred thirty-two ten-thousandths.*

Example 2 Write *ninety-nine and two hundred seven thousandths* in standard form and expanded form.

Place-Value Chart							
thousands	hundreds	tens	ones	tenths	hundredths	thousandths	ten-thousandths
0	0	9	9	2	0	7	0

Standard form: 99.207
Expanded form: $(9 \times 10) + (9 \times 1) + (2 \times 0.1) + (0 \times 0.01) + (7 \times 0.001)$

Exercises

Write each decimal in word form.

1. 2.3

2. 0.68

3. 32.501

4. 0.0036

Write each decimal in standard form and in expanded form.

5. twenty and two hundredths

6. seven and five tenths

7. three hundred four ten-thousandths

8. eleven thousandths

3-1 Skills Practice

Representing Decimals

Write each decimal in word form.

1. 6.5

2. 0.3

3. 39.2

4. 0.83

5. 5.67

6. 14.006

7. 12.001

8. 0.5214

9. 12.0905

Write each decimal in standard form and in expanded form.

10. three tenths

11. fifteen and one tenth

12. eight and four hundredths

13. seventy-two and sixteen thousandths

14. one hundred and one hundredth

15. four hundred seven thousandths

16. four hundred seven ten-thousandths

17. one hundred and one thousandth

18. Express $(2 \times 100) + (3 \times 10) + (1 \times 1) + (4 \times 0.1) + (5 \times 0.01)$ in word form.

3-1 Practice

Representing Decimals

Write each decimal in word form.

1. 0.5   2. 0.1   3. 2.49

4. 8.07   5. 0.345   6. 30.089

7. 6.0735   8. 0.0042   9. 16.375

Write each decimal in standard form and in expanded form.

10. one tenth   11. thirteen and four tenths

12. sixty-two and thirty-five hundredths

13. seven hundred twelve ten-thousandths

14. How is 611.0079 written in word form?

15. Write $(2 \times 0.1) + (8 \times 0.01)$ in word form.

16. Write $(5 \times 0.001) + (6 \times 0.0001)$ in standard form.

17. **HIKING** Pinnacles National Monument in California has 71.2 miles of hiking trails. Write this number in two other forms.

18. **ANALYZE TABLES** In the table at the right, which numbers have their last digit in the thousandths place? Explain your reasoning. Write each of these numbers in expanded form.

World Records For Smallest Animal	
Animal	**Length (cm)**
dog	7.112
hamster	4.445
newt	2.54
spider	0.0432
starfish	0.889
toad	2.3876

Source: *Guinness World Records*

3-1 **Word Problem Practice**

Representing Decimals

BASEBALL For Exercises 1–4, use the table.

The table shows lifetime batting averages for leading baseball players.

Lifetime Batting Averages for Leading Players		
Player	**Team**	**Batting Average**
Albert Pujols	St. Louis Cardinals	0.331
Derek Jeter	New York Yankees	0.316
Manny Ramirez	Boston Red Sox	0.315
Mike Piazza	San Diego Padres	0.309
Chipper Jones	Atlanta Braves	0.304

1. Write Mike Piazza's batting average in word form.

2. Which digit is in the thousandths place of each player's batting average?

3. What is the batting average for the New York Yankees player in expanded form?

4. Which player's average has a 3 in the hundredths place?

5. BUILDING When measuring board footage for some exotic woods, a carpenter must use 1.25 for thickness rather than 1 in her calculations. Write 1.25 in expanded form.

6. TRAVEL The summer camp Jason attends is exactly four hundred twenty-three and four tenths of a mile from his home. Write *four hundred twenty-three and four tenths* in standard form.

3-1 Enrichment

Decimal Letters

The letter A at the right was created by shading part of a hundreds square. There are 26 parts shaded, so the *value* of the letter A is 26 hundredths, or 0.26.

Find the value of each letter.

1.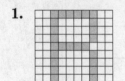
2.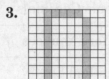
3.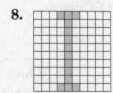
4.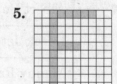
5.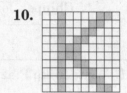

6.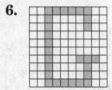
7.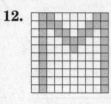
8.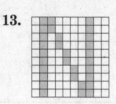
9.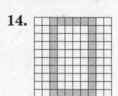
10.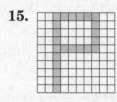

11.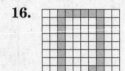
12.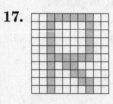
13.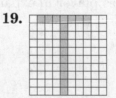
14.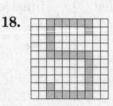
15.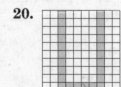

16.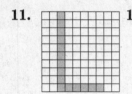
17.
18.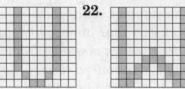
19.
20.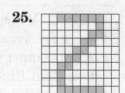

21.
22.
23.
24.
25.

26. **CHALLENGE** Use the values of the 26 letters as a set of data. What is the frequency of the value 0.26? Which value is the mode?

3-2 Lesson Reading Guide

Comparing and Ordering Decimals

Get Ready for the Lesson

Read the introduction at the top of page 142 in your textbook.
Write your answers below.

1. Which city has the longest subway system? Explain.

Read the Lesson

For Exercises 2–4, refer to the paragraph above Example 2 on page 143.

2. What are *equivalent decimals*?

3. What does it mean to annex a zero in a decimal? What happens to the value of the decimal?

4. List three decimals that are equivalent to 0.8.

5. Look at Example 2 on page 143. Why is annexing zeros used in ordering decimals?

6. What does the expression $7.6 < 7.8$ mean?

7. What symbol would you use to compare 7.6 and 7.3? Explain.

Remember What You Learned

8. Explain how using a number line to compare decimals is similar to using a number line to compare whole numbers.

Lesson 3-2

3-2 Study Guide and Intervention

Comparing and Ordering Decimals

Example 1 Use > or < to compare 68.563 and 68.5603.

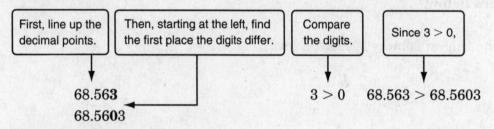

First, line up the decimal points. Then, starting at the left, find the first place the digits differ. Compare the digits. Since 3 > 0,

68.563
68.5603

3 > 0   68.563 > 68.5603

So, 68.563 is greater than 68.5603.

Example 2 Order 4.073, 4.73, 4.0073, and 4 from least to greatest.

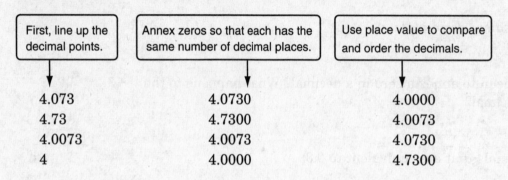

First, line up the decimal points. Annex zeros so that each has the same number of decimal places. Use place value to compare and order the decimals.

4.073	4.0730	4.0000
4.73	4.7300	4.0073
4.0073	4.0073	4.0730
4	4.0000	4.7300

The order from least to greatest is 4, 4.0073, 4.073, and 4.73.

Exercises

Use >, <, or = to compare each pair of decimals.

1. 4.08 ● 4.080   2. 0.001 ● 0.01   3. 23.659 ● 22.659

4. 50.031 ● 50.030   5. 7 ● 7.0001   6. 18.01 ● 18.010

Order each set of decimals from least to greatest.

7. 0.006, 0.6, 0.060, 6   8. 456.73, 465.32, 456.37, 456.23

Order each set of decimals from greatest to least.

9. 3.01, 3.009, 3.09, 3.0001   10. 45.303, 45.333, 45.03, 45.0003, 45.003

3-2 Skills Practice

Comparing and Ordering Decimals

Use >, <, or = to compare each pair of decimals.

1. 2.4 ● 2.04

2. 6.23 ● 6.32

3. 0.02 ● 0.020

4. 12.05 ● 12.50

5. 0.92 ● 0.095

6. 39.21 ● 39.021

7. 0.849 ● 0.0851

8. 12.1 ● 12.10

9. 21.967 ● 2.1968

10. 0.0128 ● 0.128

11. 1.4601 ● 1.460

12. 19.08 ● 19.079

13. 28.003 ● 28.03

14. 0.831 ● 0.0835

15. 39.020 ● 39.0200

16. 15.6243 ● 15.6234

17. 12.0905 ● 12.10

18. 56.7 ● 5.67

Order each set of decimals from least to greatest.

19. 1.25, 1.52, 1.02, 1.50

20. 67.39, 68.004, 67.039, 67.04

21. 15.0421, 14.52, 14.521, 15.421

22. 0.0012, 0.0211, 0.0002, 0.0022

Order each set of decimals from greatest to least.

23. 4.99, 4.001, 5.0, 4.01

24. 12.0012, 120.012, 12.012, 12.12

25. 3.5, 3.05, 3.55, 3.555

26. 45.0, 40.5, 40.09, 49.5

Lesson 3-2

3-2 Practice

Comparing and Ordering Decimals

Use >, <, or = to compare each pair of decimals.

1. 8.8 ● 8.80
2. 0.3 ● 3.0
3. 0.06 ● 0.6

4. 5.10 ● 5.01
5. 4.42 ● 4.24
6. 0.009 ● 0.9

7. 0.305 ● 0.315
8. 7.006 ● 7.060
9. 8.408 ● 8.044

10. 91.77 ● 91.770
11. 7.2953 ● 7.2593
12. 0.0826 ● 0.0286

Order each set of decimals from least to greatest.

13. 33.6, 34.01, 33.44, 34
14. 78.203, 78.34, 78.023, 78.23

Order each set of decimals from greatest to least.

15. 8.7, 8.77, 8.07, 8.777
16. 26.0999, 26.199, 25.99, 26.1909

17. **LIBRARY** Books in the library are placed on shelves in order according to their Dewey Decimal numbers. Arrange these numbers in order from least to greatest.

Book Number
943.678
943.6
943.67

18. **ANALYZE TABLES** The following table shows the amount of money Sonia spent on lunch each day this week. Order the amounts from least to greatest and then find the median amount she spent on lunch.

Day	Mon.	Tue.	Wed.	Thu.	Fri.
Amount Spent ($)	4.45	4.39	4.23	4.53	4.38

3-2 Word Problem Practice

Comparing and Ordering Decimals

MUSIC For Exercises 1–4, use the table.

The table shows the percent of the music market for each type of music.

Music Industry Sales Statistics, 2003	
Type of Music	**Percent of Market**
Pop	8.9
Country	10.4
Rock	25.2
Rap/Hip-Hop	13.3
R&B	10.6

1. Use > or < to compare the percents for pop and rap/hip-hop. Which is greater?

2. Use > or < to compare the percents for country and R&B. Which is greater?

3. If you owned a store that sells CDs, which kind of music would you want to sell, based on the table? Explain.

4. Suppose children's songs have 8.05 percent of the market. Is this greater or less than the percent for pop music? Explain.

5. **CONSTRUCTION** Alberto is setting out four boards of lumber. The lengths of the boards are 4.5 feet, 4.52 feet, 4 feet, and 4.505 feet. Order the lengths from longest to shortest.

6. **CONSTRUCTION** Ella set out a board of pine lumber that was 0.8 feet long and a board of cedar lumber that was 0.80 feet long. Alberto said the cedar board was longer. Is he correct? Explain.

3-2 Enrichment

A Look at Nutrients

The table below gives data about a few of the nutrients in an average serving of some common foods.

Food	Protein (grams)	Fat (grams)	Carbohydrates (grams)	Vitamins (milligrams)			Minerals* (milligrams)		
				B	B-1	B-2	Na	K	Ca
apple (medium)	0.3	0.5	21.1	8	0.02	0.02	1	159	10
chocolate bar (1.02 oz)	2.2	9.4	16.5	0	0.02	0.08	29	119	55
cola (12 fl oz)	0.0	0.0	40.7	0	0.00	0.00	20	7	11
hamburger (1 medium)	21.8	14.5	0.0	0	0.13	0.15	40	382	6
orange juice (8 fl oz)	1.7	0.1	26.8	97	0.20	0.05	2	474	22
peas (1/2 cup)	4.5	0.4	10.8	19	0.22	0.09	128	137	17
wheat bread (1 slice)	2.3	1.0	11.3	0	0.11	0.08	129	33	30
whole milk (8 fl oz)	8.0	8.2	11.4	2	0.09	0.40	120	370	291

*Na = sodium, K = potassium, Ca = calcium

Use the data in the table to answer each question.

1. Is there more potassium in one apple or in one serving of peas?

2. Does one serving of milk contain more fat or more carbohydrates?

3. Which foods contain less than 0.05 milligram of vitamin B-2?

4. Which foods contain an amount of carbohydrates between 15 grams and 25 grams?

5. Which food contains the least amount of calcium?

6. Which food contains the greatest amount of vitamin B-1?

7. List the foods in order of their protein content from least to greatest.

8. List the foods in order of their fat content from greatest to least.

9. Make up two questions about the data in the table. Exchange questions with a classmate. Then answer your classmate's questions.

3-2 TI-73 Activity

Ordering Decimals

Use the TI-73 calculator to sort a set of data that you have entered into a list.

Example   Sort this set of decimals from least to greatest.
5.95, 2.061, 5.6, 4.72, 2.9, 3.213, 4.97, 6.402, 5.6, 5.11,
4.99, 3.4, 2.675, 4.12, 5.006, 3.7, 4.61.

Step 1   Clear all lists.

     [2nd] [MEM] 6 [ENTER]

Step 2   Enter the numbers in list L1. Press ENTER after each number.

     [LIST]

Step 3   Sort the list L1.

     [2nd] [QUIT] [CLEAR]

     [2nd] [STAT] [▶] [ENTER]

     [2nd] [STAT] [ENTER] [ENTER]

     [LIST]

The screen shows the list of decimals ordered from least to greatest. The smallest number in the set is 2.061.

Sort the data from least to greatest. Then answer each question.
10.11, 8.61, 9.1, 10.56, 9.067, 8.11, 8.651, 8.7, 9.0, 9.8, 10.65, 8.4, 10.42, 10.019,
9.75, 9.42, 9.6, 10.5, 8.4, 10.001, 8.6, 9.65, 8.41, 8.557, 8.0, 10.9, 10.009, 10.65

1. What is the least number in the set?

2. What is the greatest number in the set?

3. What is the fifth number in the ordered list?

4. When the bottom line of the calculator's display shows L1(10)=, which number in the list is
   highlighted?

5. Are more numbers in the set greater than 9 or less than 9?

Lesson 3–2

3-3 Lesson Reading Guide

Rounding Decimals

Get Ready for the Lesson

Read the introduction at the top of page 146 in your textbook. Write your answers below.

1. Round each price to the nearest dollar.

2. How did you decide how to round each number?

3. **Make a conjecture** about how to round each cost to the nearest dime.

Read the Lesson

For Exercises 4 and 5, see Examples 1 and 3 on pages 146 and 147.

4. In Example 1, what is the underlined digit? What place is it in? Why does the 1 remain the same when the decimal is rounded?

5. In Example 3, why is the digit in the cents place underlined? Why is it increased by 1 when the decimal is rounded?

Remember What You Learned

6. Explain how to round a number. Give an example.

3-3 Study Guide and Intervention
Rounding Decimals

To round a decimal, first underline the digit to be rounded. Then look at the digit to the right of the place being rounded.

- If the digit is 4 or less, the underlined digit remains the same.
- If the digit is 5 or greater, add 1 to the underlined digit.

Example 1 Round 6.58 to the nearest tenth.

Underline the digit to be rounded.	Look at the digit to the right of the underlined digit.	Since the digit to the right is 8, add one to the underlined digit.
6.5̲8	6.5̲8	6.6

To the nearest tenth, 6.58 rounds to 6.6.

Example 2 Round 86.943 to the nearest hundredth.

Underline the digit to be rounded.	Look at the digit to the right of the underlined digit.	Since the digit is 3 and 3 < 5, the digit 4 remains the same.
86.94̲3	86.94̲3	86.94

To the nearest hundredth, 86.943 rounds to 86.94.

Exercises

Round each decimal to the indicated place-value position.

1. 3.21; tenths

2. 2.0505; thousandths

3. 6.5892; hundredths

4. 235.709; hundredths

5. 0.0914; thousandths

6. 34.35; tenths

7. 500.005; hundredths

8. 2.5134; tenths

9. 0.0052; thousandths

10. 0.0052; hundredths

11. 131.1555; thousandths

12. 232.88; tenths

Lesson 3-3

3-3 Skills Practice

Rounding Decimals

Round each decimal to the indicated place-value position.

1. 54.38; ones

2. 2.671; tenths

3. $87.01; tens

4. 12.0905; tenths

5. 441.031; ones

6. 7.892; tenths

7. 20.2093; hundredths

8. 5.5252; ones

9. 16.01; tens

10. 0.58; tenths

11. 0.2859; hundredths

12. 145.15455; thousandths

13. $10.65; ones

14. 3.0188; thousandths

15. 0.01426; thousandths

16. 4.8255; thousandths

17. 0.830528; ten-thousandths

18. 143.09354; ten-thousandths

19. 0.0523413; ten-thousandths

20. 137.892; hundredths

3-3 Practice

Rounding Decimals

Round each decimal to the indicated place-value position.

1. 8.239; tenths

2. 3.666; tenths

3. 4.47; ones

4. 10.86; ones

5. 3.299; hundredths

6. 20.687; hundredths

7. 2.3654; thousandths

8. 69.0678; thousandths

9. 5.58214; hundredths

10. 468.09156; thousandths

11. $46.49; tens

12. 1,358.761; tens

13. **LANGUAGES** In the United States, about 1.64 million people speak French as their primary language. Round this number to the nearest million.

14. **SHOPPING** The price of a pound of cooked shrimp was $3.29. How much was this to the nearest dollar?

15. **COMPUTERS** Crystal has filled up 13.57 gigabytes of her computer's hard drive. Round this amount to the nearest tenth of a gigabyte.

16. **CURRENCY** Recently, one Canadian dollar was equal to 0.835125 U.S. dollars. Round this amount of U.S. dollars to the nearest cent.

CALCULATOR A calculator will often show the results of a calculation with a very long decimal. Round each of the numbers on the calculator displays to the nearest thousandth.

17. 35.67381216

18. 1342.409448

19. .5235728864

20. **RACING** The table shows the times for a canoe paddling race at summer camp. Will it help to round these times to the nearest tenth before listing them in in order from least to greatest? Explain.

Canoe Race	
Team	**Time (h)**
Cougars	1.751
Moose	1.824
Jack Rabbits	1.665
Bears	1.739

Lesson 3-3

3-3 Word Problem Practice
Rounding Decimals

POPULATION **For Exercises 1 and 2, use the table.**

The table shows the number of people in the United States per square mile.

U.S. Population	
Year	Number of people per square mile of land area
1970	57.4
1980	64.0
1990	70.3
2000	79.6

1. Round the decimal for the number of people per square mile in 2000 to the nearest tens. Then round it to the nearest ones.

2. Round the decimal for the number of people per square mile in 1970 to the nearest tens. Then round it to the nearest ones.

EVERGLADES **For Exercises 3–7, use the following information.**

The Everglades National Park gets an average of 59.10 inches of rainfall a year. It had 1.181351 million visitors in 2004, and its budget for 2003 was $13.958 million.

3. How much rain does the Everglades National Park receive each year rounded to the nearest inch?

4. How many visitors did the park have rounded to the nearest tenth of a million?

5. How many visitors did the park have rounded to the nearest ten-thousandth of a million?

6. What is the budget to the nearest million?

7. What is the budget to the nearest hundredth of a million?

8. **SNOWBOARDING** Mike, Jake, and Aaron are buying snowboards. Mike is getting his snowboard on sale for $219.49. Jake's costs $279.97. Aaron's costs $234.95. Round each snowboard price to the nearest dollar.

3-3 Enrichment

Everybody into the Pool!

Answer each question using the "decimal pool" below.

1. Which decimal when rounded to the nearest hundredth is 0.03?

2. Which decimal when rounded to the nearest thousandth is 0.003?

3. Which two decimals when rounded to the nearest hundredth are 0.02?

4. Which five decimals when rounded to the nearest tenth are 0.2?

5. Which decimal when rounded to the nearest thousandth is 0.210?

6. Which two decimals when rounded to the nearest hundredth are 0.20?

7. Add to the pool four different decimals that when rounded to the nearest thousandth are 0.301.

8. Add to the pool a three-place decimal that when rounded to the nearest tenth is 1.0.

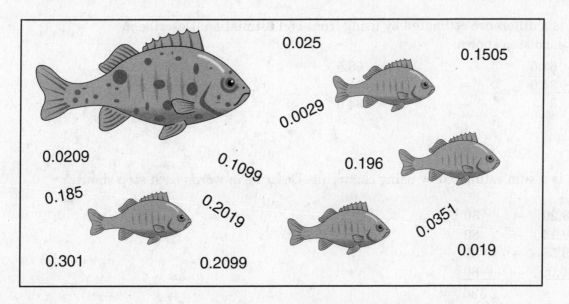

0.025   0.1505   0.0029   0.0209   0.1099   0.196   0.185   0.2019   0.0351   0.301   0.2099   0.019

9. **CHALLENGE** Suppose that you are rounding decimals to the nearest hundredth. How many three-place decimals round to 0.05? List them. How many four-place decimals do you think round to 0.05?

Lesson 3-3

3-4 Lesson Reading Guide

Estimating Sums and Differences

Get Ready for the Lesson

Read the introduction at the top of page 150 in your textbook. Write your answers below.

1. Round the number of visitors to each park to the nearest million.

2. About how many more people visit the Great Smoky Mountains National Park each year than Yosemite National Park?

Read the Lesson

3. Below is a difference estimated by rounding to the nearest tens. Describe in words each step shown.

$$
\begin{array}{rcr}
54.3 & \rightarrow & 50 \\
-\,28.7 & \rightarrow & -\,30 \\
\hline
& & 20
\end{array}
$$

4. Below is a difference estimated by using front-end estimation. Describe in words each step shown.

$$
\begin{array}{ccc}
\begin{array}{r} 68.5 \\ -\,34.9 \\ \hline 3 \end{array}
& \rightarrow &
\begin{array}{r} 68.5 \\ -\,34.9 \\ \hline 34.0 \end{array}
\end{array}
$$

5. Below is a sum estimated by using clustering. Describe in words each step shown.

$$
\begin{array}{rcr}
83.20 & \rightarrow & 80 \\
80.14 & \rightarrow & 80 \\
79.55 & \rightarrow & 80 \\
+\,80.09 & \rightarrow & +\,80 \\
\hline
& & 320
\end{array}
$$

Remember What You Learned

6. Suppose you are shopping for groceries. Which method of estimation would you use to estimate the cost of the groceries and why would you pick this method? You may want to consider accuracy, ease or speed of calculation.

3-4 Study Guide and Intervention

Estimating Sums and Differences

Estimation Methods	
Rounding	Estimate by rounding each decimal to the nearest whole number that is easy for you to add or subtract mentally.
Clustering	Estimate by rounding a group of close numbers to the same number.
Front-End Estimation	Estimate by adding or subtracting the values of the digits in the front place..

Example 1 Estimate 14.07 + 43.22 using front-end estimation.

Add the front digits.

$$\begin{array}{r} 14.07 \\ +\ 43.22 \\ \hline 5 \end{array}$$

Add the next digits.

$$\begin{array}{r} 14.07 \\ +\ 43.22 \\ \hline 57.00 \end{array}$$ An estimate for 14.07 + 43.22 is 57.

Example 2 Use clustering to estimate $7.62 + $7.89 + $8.01 + $7.99.

To use clustering, round each addend to the same number.

$$\begin{array}{rcl} 7.62 & \to & 8.00 \\ 7.89 & \to & 8.00 \\ 8.01 & \to & 8.00 \\ +\ 7.99 & \to & +\ 8.00 \\ & & \hline 32.00 \end{array}$$

An estimate for $7.62 + $7.89 + $8.01 + $7.99 is $32.

Exercises

Estimate using rounding.

1. 59.118 + 17.799

2. $45.85 + $6.82

3. 4.65 + 4.44

Estimate using clustering.

4. $0.99 + $1.15 + $0.52

5. 3.65 + 4.02 + 3.98

6. 6.87 + 6.97 + 7.39

Estimate using front-end estimation.

7. $\begin{array}{r} 81.23 \\ +\ 5.51 \end{array}$

8. $\begin{array}{r} 42.06 \\ +\ 17.39 \end{array}$

9. $\begin{array}{r} 754.23 \\ -\ 23.17 \end{array}$

Lesson 3-4

3-4 Skills Practice

Estimating Sums and Differences

Estimate using rounding.

1. 2.32 + 2.52

2. 87.146 − 24.953

3. 18.93 + 27.45

4. $46.83 + $18.60

5. $13.23 − $2.87

6. 43.058 − 15.726

Estimate using clustering.

7. 59.62 + 60.4 + 60 + 61

8. $4.79 + $5.29 + $4.99

9. 8.2 + 7.8 + 7.2 + 7.99

10. 89.04 + 87.55 + 90.101 + 91

11. 15.044 + 14.765 + 14.689

12. $1.44 + $0.86 + $1.00 + $0.70

Estimate using front-end estimation.

13.   51.62
      + 6.58

14. $233.10
      − 23.62

15.   4.57360
      − 0.58256

16.   820.1
      +   3.2

17. $102.34 + $23.00 + $32.67

18. 652.355 − 52.736

3-4 Practice

Estimating Sums and Differences

Estimate using rounding.

1. 68.99 + 22.31

2. 39.57 + 18.34

3. 81.25 − 23.16

4. 21.56 − 19.62

5. 5.69 + 3.47 + 8.02

6. 6.6 + 1.22 + 5.54

Estimate using clustering.

7. $4.56 + $4.79 + $5.21 + $5.38

8. 9.7325 + 9.55 + 10.333

9. 39.8 + 39.6 + 40.21 + 40.47

10. $69.72 + $70.44 + $70.59 + $69.56

Estimate using front-end estimation.

11. 34.87 − 29.12

12. 69.45 − 44.8

13. $78.69 + $31.49

14. $258.32 + $378.60

15. **SHOPPING** Miriam bought a basketball for $24.99 and basketball shoes for $47.79. About how much did Miriam spend on the ball and shoes?

16. **PRECIPITATION** Albuquerque gets an average of 6.35 inches of precipitation a year. Phoenix gets an average of 6.82 inches a year. About how many more inches of precipitation does Phoenix get than Albuquerque using rounding and using front-end estimation?

Lesson 3-4

3-4 Word Problem Practice

Estimating Sums and Differences

SPORTS For Exercises 1–3, use the table.

The table shows the percent of annual hospital visits due to sports injuries by males 15 to 19 years of age.

Percent of Male Sports-Related Injuries in the U.S.			
Sport	**Percent**	**Sport**	**Percent**
Basketball	25.9	Boxing, Wrestling	4.4
Football	21.3	Exercise	3.8
Baseball/softball	4.1	Bicycling	8.1
Soccer	4.6	Skateboarding	3.6

1. Use clustering to estimate the total number of hospital visits due to injuries in baseball/softball, exercising, skateboarding, and boxing.

2. Use rounding to estimate how many more visits were due to football injuries than to soccer injuries.

3. Use front-end estimation to estimate the total number of visits caused by injuries in basketball and skateboarding.

4. BASKETBALL Len dribbled a basketball for 43 seconds before Greg got the ball away. Then Greg dribbled the ball for 11.525 seconds before Len got the ball. Use front-end estimation to estimate how many more seconds Len dribbled the ball than Greg.

5. GARDENING Kevin is going to plant three new types of vegetables in his garden. The garden store sells packages of tomatillo seeds for $1.67, chili pepper seeds for $0.89, and pumpkin seeds for $2.32. Use rounding to estimate how much Kevin will spend on all three packets of seeds.

6. TRAVEL Gloria drove 53.2 miles to her grandmother's home. From her grandmother's home she drove 12.67 miles to her aunt's home. Use front-end estimation to estimate how many miles Gloria drove to get to her aunt's home. Then use rounding to estimate the number of miles again.

3-4 Enrichment

Horizontal Estimation

Many times an addition problem is given to you in *horizontal form*, with the addends written from left to right. To estimate the sum, you don't have to rewrite the addition vertically in order to line up the decimal points. Just use place value to figure out which digits are most important. Here is an example.

$3.11 + 0.4639 + 8.205$

The most important digits are in the ones place.

$3 + 0 + 8 = 11$

The next group of important digits are in the tenths place.

1 tenth + 4 tenths + 2 tenths = 7 tenths

Add to make your estimate: 11 + 7 tenths → about 11.7

Estimate each sum.

1. $7.44 + 0.2193$

2. $0.4015 + 9.3 + 3.264$

3. $0.4208 + 0.16$

4. $0.52 + 0.1 + 0.308 + 0.0294$

5. $10.2 + 0.519$

6. $12.004 + 1.5 + 4.32 + 0.1009$

7. $6.72 + 0.5037$

8. $0.805 + 1.006 + 0.4 + 2.0305$

9. $1.208 + 3.1 + 0.04 + 6.143 + 0.3075$

10. $0.9005 + 5.03 + 7.108 + 0.004 + 10.7$

This same method works when you need to estimate a sum of much greater numbers. Estimate each sum.

11. $53,129 + 420,916$

12. $6,048 + 2,137 + 509$

13. $723 + 4,106 + 4,051 + 318$

14. $7,095 + 12,402 + 3,114 + 360$

15. $650,129 + 22,018 + 107,664 + 10,509$

Lesson 3-4

3-5 Lesson Reading Guide
Adding and Subtracting Decimals

Get Ready for the Lesson

Read the introduction at the top of page 156 in your textbook.
Write your answers below.

1. Estimate the sum of the top two countries.

2. Add the digits in the same place-value position for the top two countries.

3. Compare the estimate with the actual sum. Place the decimal point in the sum.

4. Make a conjecture about how to add decimals.

Read the Lesson

For Exercises 5–7 look at the paragraph just above Example 1 on page 156 in your textbook.

5. Before you add or subtract decimals, what do you need to do?

6. Then, starting on the right, what do you do next?

7. Why do you think the first sentence of that paragraph says "in the same place-value position"? Give an example.

8. In Examples 1–5 on pages 156–158 in your textbook, the first step is to estimate the sum or difference. How does the estimate help?

Remember What You Learned

9. Tell what steps you would use to evaluate the algebraic expression $x + y$ if $x = 3.4$ and $y = 5.68$.

3-5 Study Guide and Intervention

Adding and Subtracting Decimals

To add or subtract decimals, line up the decimal points then add or subtract digits in the same place-value position. Estimate first so you know if your answer is reasonable.

Example 1 Find the sum of 61.32 + 8.26.

First, estimate the sum using front-end estimation.

$61.32 + 8.26 \rightarrow 61 + 8 = 69$

$$\begin{array}{r} 61.32 \\ + \ 8.26 \\ \hline 69.58 \end{array}$$

Since the estimate is close, the answer is reasonable.

Example 2 Find 2.65 − 0.2.

Estimate: $2.65 - 0.2 \rightarrow 3 - 0 = 3$

$$\begin{array}{r} 2.65 \\ - \ 0.20 \\ \hline 2.45 \end{array}$$ Annex a zero.

Since the estimate is close, the answer is reasonable.

Exercises

Find each sum or difference.

1. $\begin{array}{r} 2.3 \\ + \ 4.1 \\ \hline \end{array}$

2. $\begin{array}{r} \$13.67 \\ - \ 7.19 \\ \hline \end{array}$

3. $\begin{array}{r} 0.0123 \\ - \ 0.0028 \\ \hline \end{array}$

4. $\begin{array}{r} 132.346 \\ + \ 0.486 \\ \hline \end{array}$

5. $\begin{array}{r} 113.7999 \\ + \ 6.2001 \\ \hline \end{array}$

6. $\begin{array}{r} 0.0058 \\ - \ 0.0026 \\ \hline \end{array}$

7. $\begin{array}{r} \$5.63 \\ + \ 4.10 \\ \hline \end{array}$

8. $\begin{array}{r} 5.00921 \\ - 4.00013 \\ \hline \end{array}$

9. $0.2 + 5.64 + 9.005$

10. $12.36 - 4.081$

11. $216.8 - 34.055$

12. $4.62 + 3.415 + 2.4$

Lesson 3-5

3-5 Skills Practice

Adding and Subtracting Decimals

Find each sum or difference.

1.	0.581	2.	4.78	3.	9.6	4.	7.8
	+ 11		+ 6		+ 5.2		− 4.3

5.	16.79	6.	1.02	7.	20.1	8.	0.86
	− 0.51		− 0.38		+ 3.2		+ 0.38

9.	3.84	10.	4.17	11.	47.06	12.	96.293
	+ 2.69		− 2.58		− 38.27		− 68.501

Find each sum or difference.

13. 8.5 + 0.5   **14.** 8.3 + 7.9   **15.** 5.21 + 4 + 0.2

16. 3.4 + 3.2 − 6   **17.** 0.485 + 9.32   **18.** 362 − 145.9

19. 19.4 − 7.86   **20.** 4 + 8.5 + 2   **21.** 8.3 + 5.41 + 3.2

22. ALGEBRA Evaluate $b - a$ if $a = 113.04$ and $b = 241.931$.

23. ALGEBRA Evaluate $x + y$ if $x = 2.057$ and $y = 16.3$.

Find the value of each expression.

24. 3.4 − 2 + 6   **25.** $16.9 - 2^2$ **26.** 7 + 2.3 − 5.8

3-5 Practice

Adding and Subtracting Decimals

Find each sum.

1. $5.4 + 6.5$ 2. $6.0 + 3.8$ 3. $3.65 + 4$

4. $52.47 + 13.21$ 5. $91.64 + 19.5$ 6. $0.675 + 28$

Find each difference.

7. $7.8 - 4.5$ 8. $69 - 12.88$ 9. $17.46 - 6.79$

10. $74 - 59.29$ 11. $87.31 - 25.09$ 12. $19.75 - 12.98$

ALGEBRA Evaluate each expression if $a = 219.6$ and $b = 12.024$.

13. $a - b$ 14. $b + a$ 15. $a - 13.45 - b$

Find the value of each expression.

16. $4.3 + 6 \times 7$ 17. $3^2 - 2.55$ 18. $19.7 - 4^2$

19. **BIKE RIDING** The table shows the distances the members of two teams rode their bicycles for charity.

   a. How many total miles did Lori's team ride?

   b. How many more miles did Lori's team ride than Tati's team?

Distances Ridden for Charity	
Lori's Team	**Tati's Team**
Lori 13.8 mi	Tati 13.6 mi
Marcus 11.8 mi	Luis 15.1 mi
Hassan 15.4 mi	

Lesson 3-5

3-5 Word Problem Practice

Adding and Subtracting Decimals

1. **MICE** The average length of the head and body of a western harvest mouse is 2.9 inches. The average length of the tail is 2.8 inches. First, estimate the total length of the mouse. Then find the actual total length.

2. **MUSIC** A piano solo on a CD is 5.33 minutes long. A guitar solo is 9.67 minutes long. How much longer is the guitar solo than the piano solo? First estimate the difference. Then find the actual difference.

3. **WHALES** The average length of a humpback whale is 13.7 meters. The average length of a killer whale is 6.85 meters. How much longer is the humpback whale than the killer whale?

4. **GARDENING** Alan is connecting three garden hoses to make one longer hose. The green hose is 6.25 feet long, the orange hose is 5.755 feet long, and the black hose is 6.5 feet long. First, estimate the total length. Then find the actual total length.

5. **ASTRONOMY** Distance in space can be measured in astronomical units, or AU. Jupiter is 5.2 AU from the Sun. Pluto is 39.223 AU from the Sun. How much closer to the Sun is Jupiter than Pluto?

6. **ALGEBRA** It is x miles from James City to Huntley and y miles from Huntley to Grover. How many miles is it from James City to Grover? To find out, evaluate $x + y$ if $x = 4.23$ and $y = 16.876$.

3-5 Enrichment

Currency

The currency used in the United States is the US dollar. Each dollar is divided into 100 cents. Most countries have their own currencies. On January 1, 2002, 12 countries in Europe converted to a common monetary unit that is called the *euro*.

The symbol, €, is used to indicate the euro.

The exchange rate between dollars and euros changes every day.

$1.00 is worth about 0.85€.

EXERCISES Add or subtract to solve each problem.

1. Henry bought a pair of shoes for €34.75 and a pair of pants for €21.49. How much money did he spend?

2. Louis receives €10.50 a week for doing his chores. His sister is younger and has fewer chores. She receives €5.25. How much money do Louis and his sister receive together in one week?

3. A gallon of Brand A of vanilla ice cream costs €5.49. A gallon of Brand B vanilla ice cream costs €4.87. How much money will Luca save if he buys Brand A instead of Brand B?

4. Michael passed up a pair of jeans that cost €29.50 and decided to buy a pair that were only €15.86. How much money did he save by buying the less expensive jeans?

5. Jesse's favorite magazine costs €1.75 at the store. If he buys a subscription, each issue is only 0.37€. How much money will Jesse save on each issue if he buys a subscription?

6. Layla wants to buy a CD for €11.99 and a book for €6.29. She has €15.00. How much more money does she need to buy the CD and book?

7. **CHALLENGE** Lynne's lunch came to €4.00. Her drink was €1.50. How much did she spend total? What would be the equivalent dollar amount?

8. **CHALLENGE** At the grocery store, Jaden purchased a box of cereal for $3.55 and a gallon of milk for $2.89. He gave the cashier $10.00. How much change did he receive? What would be the equivalent euro amount?

Lesson 3-5

3-5 Scientific Calculator Activity

Adding and Subtracting Decimals

A calculator may be helpful in solving equations with decimals.

Example 1 $0.628 + 7.314$

Enter: .628 $+$ 7.314 $\boxed{\text{ENTER}}$ 7.942

The solution is 7.942.

Example 2 $2.701 + 35 - 24.1$

Enter: 2.701 $+$ 35 $-$ 24.1 $\boxed{\text{ENTER}}$ 13.601

The solution is 13.601.

Add or subtract.

1. $8.2 - 3.57$

2. $86.327 + 0.38$

3. $10.2 - 10.2$

4. $37 + 68.31$

5. $0.3 + 2.01 + 8.4$

6. $10 - 0.03$

7. $0.084 + 1.4 - 0.72$

8. $3 + 0.4 - 0.001$

9. $800 + 0.080 + 0.0008$

10. $10 - 0.10 - 0.001 - 0.0001$

Evaluate each expression if $a = 8.24$, $b = 7.1$, and $c = 0.001$.

11. $a - b$

12. $b + c$

13. $a + b - c$

14. $a - c + b$

15. **CHALLENGE** Evaluate $r^2 - 3s^2$ if $r = 6.25$ and $s = 1.5$.

3-6 Lesson Reading Guide

Multiplying Decimals by Whole Numbers

Get Ready for the Lesson

Read the introduction at the top of page 163 in your textbook. Write your answers below.

1. Use the addition problem and the estimate to find $2 \times \$4.92$.

2. Write an addition problem, an estimate, and a multiplication problem to find the total over 3 days, 4 days, and 5 days.

3. **MAKE A CONJECTURE** about how to find 5.35×4.

Read the Lesson

4. When multiplying a whole number and a decimal, it is very important that the decimal point in the product is in the right place. What are two methods for determining the placement of the decimal point in the product?

5. If you place the decimal point in the product of a whole number and a decimal by counting decimal places, how is this done?

6. What does it mean to annex zeros in the product? Why is it sometimes necessary to do this?

Remember What You Learned

7. Work with a partner. Explain the difference between standard form and scientific notation, and give examples of each.

3-6 Study Guide and Intervention

Multiplying Decimals by Whole Numbers

When you multiply a decimal by a whole number, you multiply the numbers as if you were multiplying all whole numbers. Then you use estimation or you count the number of decimal places to decide where to place the decimal point. If there are not enough decimal places in the product, annex zeros to the left.

Example 1 Find 6.25 × 5.

Method 1 Use estimation.

Round 6.25 to 6.
6.25 × 5 → 6 × 5 or 30

$$\begin{array}{r} 1\ 2 \\ 6.25 \\ \underline{\times\quad 5} \\ 31.25 \end{array}$$

Since the estimate is 30 place the decimal point after 31.

Method 2 Count decimal places.

$$\begin{array}{r} 6.25 \\ \underline{\times\quad 5} \\ 31.25 \end{array}$$

There are two places to the right of the decimal point.

Count the same number of decimal places from right to left.

Example 2 Find 3 × 0.0047.

$$\begin{array}{r} 2 \\ 0.0047 \\ \underline{\times\qquad 3} \\ 0.0141 \end{array}$$

There are four decimal places.

Annex a zero on the left of 141 to make four decimal places.

Example 3 Find 6.3 × 1,000.

Method 1 Use paper and pencil.

$$\begin{array}{r} 1,000 \\ \underline{\times\ 6.3} \\ 3\ 000 \\ \underline{60\ 000} \\ 6,300.0 \end{array}$$

Method 2 Use mental math.

Move the decimal point to the right the same number of zeros that are in 1,000 or 3 places.

6.3 × 1,000 = 6,300

Exercises

Multiply.

1. 8.03 × 3

2. 6 × 12.6

3. 2 × 0.012

4. 0.0008 × 9

5. 2.32 × 10

6. 6.8 × 100

7. 5.2 × 1000

8. 1.412 × 100

3-6 Skills Practice

Multiplying Decimals by Whole Numbers

Multiply.

1. 1.5
$\times 3$

2. 0.9
$\times 6$

3. 0.45
$\times 5$

4. 3.12
$\times 8$

5. 3.47
$\times 5$

6. 2.08
$\times 6$

7. 9.14
$\times 2$

8. 0.82
$\times 9$

9. 6.3
$\times 9$

10. 0.02
$\times 3$

11. 9.12
$\times 4$

12. 27.3
$\times 8$

13. 4.007
$\times 4$

14. 3.13
$\times 3$

15. 5.02
$\times 8$

16. 6.31
$\times 6$

17. 8.01
$\times 5$

18. 4.325
$\times 7$

19. 0.762
$\times 2$

20. 0.08
$\times 8$

21. 6×3.04

22. 2.6×9

23. 13×2.5

24. 1.006×4

25. Evaluate $42.3t$ if $t = 110$.

26. Evaluate $231a$ if $a = 3.6$

27. 3.2×10

28. 4.5×100

29. $6.2 \times 1,000$

3-6 Practice

Multiplying Decimals by Whole Numbers

Multiply.

1. 0.8×6 **2.** 0.7×4 **3.** 1.9×5 **4.** 3.4×9

5. 6×3.4 **6.** 5.2×9 **7.** 0.6×6 **8.** 4×0.8

9. 5×0.05 **10.** 3×0.029 **11.** 0.0027×15 **12.** 0.0186×92

ALGEBRA Evaluate each expression.

13. $5.02h$ if $h = 36$ **14.** $72.33j$ if $j = 3$ **15.** $21k$ if $k = 24.09$

Multiply.

16. 4.23×100 **17.** $3.7 \times 1,000$ **18.** 2.6×10 **19.** $4.2 \times 1,000$

20. 1.23×100 **21.** $5.14 \times 1,000$ **22.** 6.7×10 **23.** $7.89 \times 1,000$

24. SHOPPING Basketballs sell for $27.99 each at the Super D and for $21.59 each at the Bargain Spot. If the coach buys a dozen basketballs, how much can he save by buying them at the Bargain Spot? Justify your answer.

25. SCHOOL Jaimie purchases 10 pencils at the school bookstore. They cost $0.30 each. How much did she spend on pencils?

44

3-6 Word Problem Practice

Multiplying Decimals by Whole Numbers

1. COOKING Norberto uses three 14.7 oz cans of chicken broth when he makes his delicious tortilla soup. How many total ounces of chicken broth does he use?

2. TIME Amanda works on a farm out in the hills. It takes her 2.25 hours to drive to town and back. She usually goes to town twice a week to get supplies. How much time does Amanda spend driving if she takes 8 trips to town each month?

3. EXERCISE The local health club is advertising a special for new members: no initiation fee to join and only $34.50 per month for the first year. If Andy joins the health club for one year, how much will he spend on membership?

4. BIKING In order to train for a cross-state biking trip, Julie rides her bike 34.75 miles five times a week. How many total miles does she ride each week?

5. MONEY David wants to buy 16 bolts from a bin at the hardware store. Each bolt costs $0.03. How much will David pay for the bolts?

6. INSECTS One wing of a Royal Moth is 0.75 inch across. How wide is the moth's wingspan when both wings are open?

7. COSTUMES KJ is making costumes for this year's samba parade. The pattern she is using calls for 2.125 yards of fabric for each costume. How many yards of fabric will she need to make 34 costumes?

8. POOL PASSES The girl scouts are going to the pool. It will cost them $2.50 per person to go and there are 10 people going. What will the total cost be?

3-6 Enrichment

Multiplying by 10, 100, and 1,000

Can you see a pattern in these multiplications?

5.931	5.931	5.931
$\times$ 10	$\times$ 100	$\times$ 1,000
59.310 = 59.31	593.100 = 593.1	5,931.000 = 5,931

When you multiply a number by 10, 100, or 1,000, the product contains the same digits as the original number. However, the decimal point "moves" according to these rules.

multiply by 10 $\longrightarrow$ move to the right one place
multiply by 100 $\longrightarrow$ move to the right two places
multiply by 1,000 $\longrightarrow$ move to the right three places

Many people use this fact as a mental math strategy.

Find each product mentally.

1. 10×7.402

2. 100×7.402

3. $1,000 \times 7.402$

4. 10×0.84

5. $1,000 \times 0.5362$

6. 100×3.83

7. 24.07×10

8. $1.918 \times 1,000$

9. 0.075×100

10. 6.1×10

11. 0.0046×100

12. $0.005 \times 1,000$

Now you can use this mental math strategy to estimate some products. The secret is to recognize when one of the factors is fairly close to 10, 100, or 1,000. An example is shown at the right.

$$32.83 \longrightarrow 32.83$$
$$\times 97 \longrightarrow \times 100$$
$$3,283$$

So, 32.83×97 is about 3,283.

Estimate by rounding one number to 10, 100, or 1,000.

13. 6.57×9

14. 14.32×96

15. $1,225 \times 3.548$

16. 0.6214×11.05

17. 98.04×26.331

18. 0.0358×9.3145

19. CHALLENGE Find the product $1,000 \times 16.5$ mentally.
How is this different from the other exercises on this page?

3-7 **Lesson Reading Guide**

Multiplying Decimals

Get Ready for the Lesson

Read the introduction at the top of page 169 in your textbook.
Write your answers below.

1. The average weight of each block is 2.5 tons. The expression 2.3×2.5 can be used to find the total weight, in millions of tons, of the blocks in the pyramid's base. Estimate the product of 2.3 and 2.5

2. Multiply 23 by 25.

3. **MAKE A CONJECTURE** about how you can use your answers in Exercises 2 and 3 to find the product of 2.3 and 2.5?

4. What is the total weight of the blocks in the pyramid's base?

5. Use your conjecture in Exercise 3 to find 1.7×5.4. Explain each step.

Read the Lesson

6. When multiplying decimals, what is the relationship between the number of decimal places in each factor and the number of decimal places in the product?

7. Look at Exercises 1 and 2 above and the answers for these exercises.
   a. How is 25 related to 2.5 tons?
   b. How is 23 related to 2.3?
   c. What is the actual weight if 2.3 is multiplied by 2.5?
   d. How is 575 related to the actual weight of the blocks?

Remember What You Learned

8. In situations where you are multiplying decimals by whole numbers it is easy to think of the calculation as adding the same value multiple times. What does it mean to multiply decimals? Describe some situations where you would need to multiply decimals.

Lesson 3-7

3-7 Study Guide and Intervention

Multiplying Decimals

When you multiply a decimal by a decimal, multiply the numbers as if you were multiplying all whole numbers. To decide where to place the decimal point, find the sum of the number of decimal places in each factor. The product has the same number of decimal places.

Example 1 Find 5.2×6.13.

Estimate: 5×6 or 30

$$
\begin{array}{r}
5.2 \longleftarrow \text{one decimal place} \\
\times\ 6.13 \longleftarrow \text{two decimal places} \\
\hline
156 \\
52 \\
\underline{312} \\
31.876 \longleftarrow \text{three decimal places}
\end{array}
$$

The product is 31.876. Compared to the estimate, the product is reasonable.

Example 2 Evaluate $0.023t$ if $t = 2.3$.

$0.023t = 0.023 \times 2.3$ Replace t with 2.3.

$$
\begin{array}{r}
0.023 \longleftarrow \text{three decimal places} \\
\times\ 2.3 \longleftarrow \text{one decimal place} \\
\hline
69 \\
\underline{46} \\
0.0529 \longleftarrow \text{Annex a zero to make four decimal places.}
\end{array}
$$

Exercises

Multiply.

1. 7.2×2.1

2. 4.3×8.5

3. 2.64×1.4

4. 14.23×8.21

5. 5.01×11.6

6. 9.001×4.2

ALGEBRA Evaluate each expression if $x = 5.07$, $y = 1.5$, and $z = 0.403$.

7. $3.2x + y$

8. $yz + x$

9. $z \times 7.06 - y$

3-7 Skills Practice

Multiplying Decimals

Lesson 3-7

Multiply.

1. 0.3×0.5

2. 1.2×2.1

3. 2.5×6.7

4. 0.4×8.3

5. 2.3×1.21

6. 0.6×0.91

7. 6.5×0.04

8. 8.54×3.27

9. 5.02×1.07

10. 0.003×2.9

11. 0.93×6.8

12. 7.1×0.004

13. 3.007×6.1

14. 2.52×0.15

15. 2.6×5.46

16. 16.25×1.3

17. 3.5×24.09

18. 0.025×17.1

19. 11.04×6.18

20. 14.83×16.7

21. 27.1×10.105

ALGEBRA Evaluate each expression if $x = 2.1$, $y = 0.031$, and $z = 3.05$.

22. $xy + z$

23. $y + xz$

24. $x \times 13.55 - y$

3-7 Practice

Multiplying Decimals

Multiply.

1. 0.3×0.9 **2.** 2.6×1.7 **3.** 1.09×5.4 **4.** 17.2×12.86

5. 0.56×0.03 **6.** 4.9×0.02 **7.** 2.07×2.008 **8.** 26.02×2.006

ALGEBRA **Evaluate each expression if $r = 0.034$, $s = 4.05$, and $t = 2.6$.**

9. $5.027 + 4.68r$ **10.** $2.9s - 3.7t$ **11.** $4.13s + r$ **12.** rst

13. MINING A mine produces 42.5 tons of coal per hour. How much coal will the mine produce in 9.5 hours?

14. SHOPPING Ms. Morgan bought 3.5 pounds of bananas at $0.51 a pound and 4.5 pounds of pineapple at $1.19 a pound. How much did she pay for the bananas and pineapple?

3-7 Word Problem Practice

Multiplying Decimals

Lesson 3–7

1. **GIFTS** Colin is filling 4.5 ounce bottles with lavender bubble bath that he made for gifts. He was able to fill 7.5 bottles. How many ounces of bubble bath did he make?

2. **GROCERY** Iona's favorite peaches are $2.50 per pound at the local farmers' market. She bought 3.5 pounds of the peaches. How much did she spend?

3. **SHOPPING** Jennifer is buying new school clothes. The items she wants to buy add up to $132.50 before sales tax. Sales tax is calculated by multiplying the total amount by 0.08. What is the amount of sales tax for the items?

4. **DRIVING** Ana bought a van that holds 20.75 gallons of gas and gets an average of 15.5 miles per gallon. How many miles can she expect to go on a full tank?

5. **INCOME** Ishi makes $8.50 an hour rolling sushi at Kyoto Japanese Restaurant. His paycheck shows that he worked 20.88 hours over the past two weeks. How much did Ishi make before taxes?

6. **TRAVEL** Manny is on vacation in France. He rented a car to drive 233.3 kilometers from Paris to Brussels and wants to figure out the distance in miles. To convert from kilometers to miles, he needs to multiply the total kilometers by 0.62. How many miles will Manny drive?

3-7 Enrichment

A Logic Puzzle

Here is a puzzle that will help you brush up on your logical thinking skills.

The product 3.3×8.1 is in both the circle and the triangle, but not in the square. Place the product in the diagram at the right.

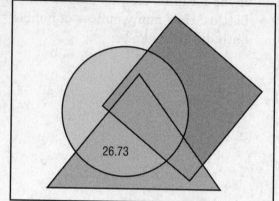

$$\begin{array}{r} 8.1 \\ \times\ 3.3 \\ \hline 2\,4\,3 \\ \underline{2\,4\,3\ \ } \\ 2\,6.73 \end{array}$$ ← Write 26.73 in the correct region of the diagram.

Use the given information to place the product in the diagram above.

1. The product 14.19×1.3 is in both the triangle and the square, but not in the circle.

2. The product 0.08×2.7 is in the triangle, but not in the circle or the square.

3. The product 1.24×0.16 is not in the circle, the square, or the triangle.

4. The product 2.2×0.815 is in both the square and the circle, but not in the triangle.

5. The product 0.02×0.03 is in the circle, but not the triangle or the square.

6. The product 21.7×0.95 is in the circle, the square, and the triangle.

7. The product 2.5×12.8 is in the square, but not the circle or triangle.

8. If you did all the calculations correctly, the sum of all the numbers in the diagram should be a "nice" number. What is the sum?

52

3-8 Lesson Reading Guide

Dividing Decimals by Whole Numbers

Get Ready for the Lesson

Complete the Mini Lab at the top of page 173 in your textbook.
Write your answers below.

Use base-ten blocks to show each quotient.

1. $3.4 \div 2$

2. $4.2 \div 3$

3. $5.6 \div 4$

Find each whole number quotient.

4. $34 \div 2$

5. $42 \div 3$

6. $56 \div 4$

7. Compare and contrast the quotients in Exercises 1–3 with the quotients in Exercises 4–6.

8. **MAKE A CONJECTURE** Write a rule for dividing a decimal by a whole number.

Read the Lesson

9. In the equation $4.8 \div 8 = 0.6$, how can you check to see if the division sentence is true?

10. Where do you place the decimal point in the quotient when dividing by a whole number?

Remember What You Learned

11. Work with a partner. Pretend your partner missed the class that covered this lesson. Explain to your partner the method for knowing where to place the decimal point when you are dividing with decimals.

3-8 Study Guide and Intervention

Dividing Decimals by Whole Numbers

When you divide a decimal by a whole number, place the decimal point in the quotient above the decimal point in the dividend. Then divide as you do with whole numbers.

Example 1 Find $8.73 \div 9$.

Estimate: $9 \div 9 = 1$

$$
\begin{array}{r}
0.97 \\
9\overline{)8.73} \\
-0 \\
\hline
8\,7 \\
-8\,1 \\
\hline
63 \\
-63 \\
\hline
0
\end{array}
$$

Place the decimal point directly above the decimal point in the quotient.

Divide as with whole numbers.

$8.73 \div 9 = 0.97$ Compared to the estimate, the quotient is reasonable.

Example 2 Find $8.58 \div 12$.

Estimate: $10 \div 10 = 1$

$$
\begin{array}{r}
0.715 \\
12\overline{)8.580} \\
-8\,4 \\
\hline
18 \\
-12 \\
\hline
60 \\
-60 \\
\hline
0
\end{array}
$$

Place the decimal point.

Annex a zero to continue dividing.

$8.58 \div 12 = 0.715$ Compared to the estimate, the quotient is reasonable.

Exercises

Divide.

1. $9.2 \div 4$

2. $4.5 \div 5$

3. $8.6 \div 2$

4. $2.89 \div 4$

5. $3.2 \div 4$

6. $7.2 \div 3$

7. $7.5 \div 5$

8. $3.25 \div 5$

3-8 Skills Practice

Dividing Decimals by Whole Numbers

Divide. Round to the nearest tenth if necessary.

1. $9.6 \div 3$

2. $5.15 \div 5$

3. $16.08 \div 2$

4. $24.64 \div 7$

5. $132.22 \div 11$

6. $142.4 \div 16$

7. $79.2 \div 9$

8. $47.4 \div 15$

9. $217.14 \div 21$

10. $34.65 \div 5$

11. $20.72 \div 8$

12. $72.6 \div 10$

13. $57.48 \div 15$

14. $264.5 \div 25$

15. $317.594 \div 34$

16. $122.32 \div 11$

17. $42.48 \div 18$

18. $323.316 \div 24$

Lesson 3-8

3-8 Practice

Dividing Decimals by Whole Numbers

Divide. Round to the nearest tenth if necessary.

1. $25.2 \div 4$ **2.** $147.2 \div 8$ **3.** $5.69 \div 7$ **4.** $13.28 \div 3$

5. $22.5 \div 15$ **6.** $65.28 \div 12$ **7.** $243.83 \div 32$ **8.** $654.29 \div 19$

9. WEATHER What is the average January precipitation in Arches National Park? Round to the nearest hundredth if necessary.

January Precipitation in Arches National Park								
Year	1997	1998	1999	2000	2001	2002	2003	2004
Precipitation (in.)	1.09	0.013	0.54	0.80	0.89	0.24	0.11	0.16

Source: National Park Service

10. SHOPPING A 3-pack of boxes of juice costs $1.09. A 12-pack of boxes costs $4.39. A case of 24 boxes costs $8.79. Which is the best buy? Explain your reasoning.

3-8 Word Problem Practice

Dividing Decimals by Whole Numbers

1. **ENTERTAINMENT** Frank, Gina, Judy, and Connie are splitting their dinner bill. After tip, the total is $30.08. How much does each owe if they split the bill four ways?

2. **FOOD** There are 25 servings in a 12.5 ounce bottle of olive oil. How many ounces are in a serving?

3. **RUNNING** Isabella has found that she stays the most fit by running various distances and terrains throughout the week. On Mondays she runs 2.5 miles, on Tuesdays 4.6 miles, on Thursdays 6.75 miles, and on Saturdays 4.8 miles. What is the average distance Isabella runs on each of the days that she runs? Round to the nearest hundredth of a mile.

4. **BUSINESS** Katherine spends $1,089.72 each month for rent and supplies to run her hair salon. If she charges $18 for a haircut, how many haircuts must Katherine do to cover her monthly expenses? Round to the nearest whole number.

5. **CONSTRUCTION** It took Steve and his construction crew 8 months to build a house. After expenses, he was left with $24,872.67 for himself. On average, how much did Steve make per month? Round to the nearest dollar.

6. **GRADES** Shane wants to figure out what grade he is getting in math. His test scores were 85.6, 78.5, 92.5, 67, and 83.7. What was his average test score? What grade will he receive?

Grade	Average Score
A	90 – 100
B	80 – 89
C	70 – 79
D	60 – 69
F	50 – 59

Lesson 3-8

3-8 Enrichment

Unit Pricing

The **unit price** of an item is the cost of the item given in terms of one *unit* of the item. The unit might be something that you count, like jars or cans, or it might be a unit of measure, like ounces or pounds. You can find a unit price using this formula.

unit price = cost of item ÷ number of units

For example, you find the unit price of the tuna in the ad at the right by finding the quotient 0.89 ÷ 6. The work is shown below the ad. Rounding the quotient to the nearest cent, the unit price is $0.15 *per ounce*.

TUNA
89¢
6 ounce can

$$\begin{array}{r} 0.148 \\ 6\overline{)0.890} \\ \underline{6} \\ 29 \\ \underline{24} \\ 50 \\ \underline{48} \\ 2 \end{array}$$

Find a unit price for each item.

1.
5-pound bag
CARROTS
$1.29

2.
18-ounce jar
PEANUT BUTTER
$2.49

3.
Grade A Jumbo
EGGS
Dozen $1.59

Give two different unit prices for each item.

4.
Frozen BURRITOS
5-ounce pkg
2 for $1.39

5.
Purr-fect
CAT FOOD
3/$1 3-ounce can

6.
Old Tyme
SPAGHETTI SAUCE
12-ounce jars 2/$3

Circle the better buy.

7.
Mozarella Cheese	Mozarella Cheese
3/$4	2/$3
10-ounce pkg	18-ounce pkg

8.
Dee-light Chicken Wings	Top Q Chicken Wings
$9.99	$2.29
5-pound bag	18-ounce bag

3-9 Lesson Reading Guide

Dividing by Decimals

Get Ready for the Lesson

Complete the Mini Lab at the top of page 179 in your textbook.
Write your answers below.

Use a calculator to find each quotient.

1. Describe a pattern among the division problems and their quotients for each set.

2. Use the pattern in Set A to find 36 ÷ 0.0009 without a calculator.

3. Use the pattern in Set B to find 0.0036 ÷ 9 without a calculator.

4. Use the pattern in Set C to find 0.0036 ÷ 0.0009 without a calculator.

5. How could you find 0.042 ÷ 0.07 without a calculator?

Read the Lesson

6. When dividing decimals, what happens to the decimal point in the divisor and the dividend when you multiply both by the same power of 10?

7. Without doing any dividing, describe what you must do to start dividing 0.07 by 1.5.

Remember What You Learned

8. Write a short song or come up with a clever saying that will help you remember that whatever change you make to the decimal point of the divisor you must also make to the decimal point of the dividend.

Lesson 3-9

3-9 **Study Guide and Intervention**

Dividing by Decimals

When you divide a decimal by a decimal, multiply both the divisor and the dividend by the same power of ten. Then divide as with whole numbers.

Example 1 Find $10.14 \div 5.2$.

Estimate: $10 \div 5 = 2$

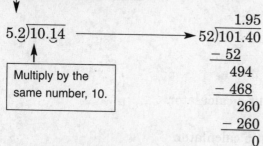

$$\begin{array}{r} 1.95 \\ 52\overline{)101.40} \\ -52 \\ \hline 494 \\ -468 \\ \hline 260 \\ -260 \\ \hline 0 \end{array}$$

Place the decimal point.
Divide as with whole numbers.

Annex a zero to continue.

10.14 divided by 5.2 is 1.95.

Check: $1.95 \times 5.2 = 10.14$ ✓

Compare to the estimate.

Example 2 Find $4.09 \div 0.02$.

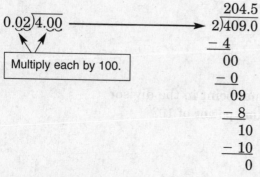

$$\begin{array}{r} 204.5 \\ 2\overline{)409.0} \\ -4 \\ \hline 00 \\ -0 \\ \hline 09 \\ -8 \\ \hline 10 \\ -10 \\ \hline 0 \end{array}$$

Place the decimal point.
Divide.

Write a zero in the dividend
and continue to divide.

$4.09 \div 0.02$ is 204.5.

Check: $204.5 \times 0.02 = 4.09$ ✓

Exercises

Divide.

1. $9.8 \div 1.4$

2. $4.41 \div 2.1$

3. $16.848 \div 0.72$

4. $8.652 \div 1.2$

5. $0.5 \div 0.001$

6. $9.594 \div 0.06$

3-9 Skills Practice

Dividing by Decimals

Divide.

1. $4.86 \div 0.2$

2. $2.52 \div 0.7$

3. $14.4 \div 1.2$

4. $17.1 \div 3.8$

5. $3.96 \div 1.32$

6. $628.2 \div 34.9$

7. $0.105 \div 0.5$

8. $1.296 \div 0.16$

9. $3.825 \div 2.5$

10. $8.253 \div 0.5$

11. $0.9944 \div 0.8$

12. $1.50048 \div 0.32$

13. $13.59 \div 0.75$

14. $4.4208 \div 1.8$

15. $16.1604 \div 4.02$

16. $160.3639 \div 25.1$

17. $246.3293 \div 13.3$

18. $106.288 \div 6.5$

Lesson 3-9

3-9 Practice

Dividing by Decimals

Divide.

1. $12.92 \div 3.4$

2. $22.47 \div 0.7$

3. $0.025 \div 0.5$

4. $7.224 \div 0.08$

5. $0.855 \div 9.5$

6. $0.9 \div 0.12$

7. $3.0084 \div 0.046$

8. $0.0868 \div 0.007$

9. **WHALES** After its first day of life, a baby blue whale started growing. It grew 47.075 inches. If the average baby blue whale grows at a rate of 1.5 inches a day, for how many days did the baby whale grow, to the nearest tenth of a day?

10. **LIZARDS** The two largest lizards in the United States are the Gila Monster and the Chuckwalla. The average Gila Monster is 0.608 meter long. The average Chuckwalla is 0.395 meters long. How many times longer is the Gila Monster than the Chuckwalla to the nearest hundredth?

3-9 Word Problem Practice

Dividing by Decimals

MARATHON For Exercises 1 and 2, use the table that shows course records for the Boston Marathon.

Course Records for the Boston Marathon			
Division	**Record-holder**	**Year**	**Time (hours)**
Men's Open	Cosmas Ndeti	1994	2.121
Women's Open	Margaret Okayo	2002	2.345
Men's Wheelchair	Ernst Van Dyk	2004	1.305
Women's Wheelchair	Jean Driscoll	1994	1.523

1. The Boston Marathon is 26.2 miles. Use the times shown in the table to calculate the miles per hour for each division winner. Round to the nearest thousandth.

2. To the nearest hundredth, how many times greater was the men's open time than the women's wheelchair time?

3. DRIVING The Martinez family drove 48.7 miles to the river. It took them 1.2 hours to get there. How fast did they drive? Round to the nearest whole number.

4. SHOPPING Nikki is buying some refrigerator magnets for her friends. Her total bill is $16.80. If magnets are $0.80 each, how many magnets is she buying?

5. SCALE MODEL Matt is making a scale model of a building. The model is 3.4 feet tall. The actual building is 41.48 feet tall. How many times smaller is the model than the actual building?

6. COOKING Yori has 14.25 cups of cupcake batter. If each cupcake uses 0.75 cup of batter, how many cupcakes can Yori make?

3-9 Enrichment

It's in the Cards

Below each set of cards, a quotient is given. Use the digits on the cards to form a division sentence with that quotient. Use as many zeros as you need to get the correct number of decimal places. For example, this is how to find a division for the cards at the right.

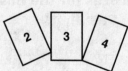

Quotient: 0.0008

You know that $24 \div 3 = 8$.
So, one division is $0.0024 \div 30 = 0.0008$.

1.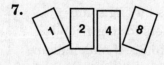

Quotient: 0.009

2.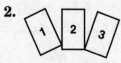

Quotient: 0.04

3.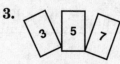

Quotient: 0.0005

4.

Quotient: 0.0074

5.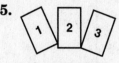

Quotient: 0.0155

6.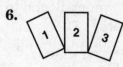

Quotient: 0.0025

7.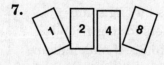

Quotient: 0.0004

8.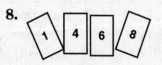

Quotient: 0.03

9.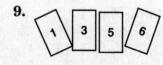

Quotient: 0.005

10.

Quotient: 20.65

11.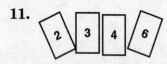

Quotient: 0.0208

12.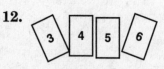

Quotient: 0.08

13. CHALLENGE Use the cards at the right. Write four *different* divisions that have the quotient 0.4.

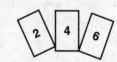

3-10 Study Guide and Intervention

Problem-Solving Investigation: Reasonable Answers

When solving problems, one strategy that is helpful is to *determine reasonable answers*. If you are solving a problem with big numbers, or a problem with information that you are unfamiliar with, it may be helpful to look back at your answer to determine if it is reasonable.

You can use the *determine reasonable answers* strategy, along with the following four-step problem solving plan to solve a problem.

1 Understand – Read and get a general understanding of the problem.

2 Plan – Make a plan to solve the problem and estimate the solution.

3 Solve – Use your plan to solve the problem.

4 Check – Check the reasonableness of your solution.

Example **ANIMALS** The average height of a male chimpanzee is 1.2 meters, and the average height of a female chimpanzee is 1.1 meters. What is a reasonable height in feet of a male chimpanzee?

Understand We know the average height in meters of a male chimpanzee.

We need to find a reasonable height in feet.

Plan One meter is very close to one yard. One yard is equal to 3 feet. So, estimate how many feet would be in 1.2 yards.

Solve 1.2 yards would be more than 3 feet, but less than 6 feet.

So, a reasonable average height of a male chimpanzee is about 4 feet.

Check Since 1.2 yd = 3.6 ft, the answer of 4 feet is reasonable.

Exercise

SHOPPING Alexis wants to buy 2 bracelets for $6.95 each, 1 pair of earrings for $4.99, and 2 necklaces for $8.95 each. Does she need $40 or will $35 be more reasonable? Explain.

Lesson 3–10

3-10 Skills Practice

Problem-Solving Investigation: Reasonable Answers

Solve. Use the determine reasonable answers strategy.

1. **ANIMALS** A male African elephant weights 6.5 tons. What is a reasonable weight in pounds of a male African elephant?

2. **AWARDS** The school auditorium holds 3,600 people. Is it reasonable to offer each of the 627 students five tickets for family and friends to attend the awards ceremony? Explain.

3. **POPULATION** Use the graph at the right to determine whether 600, 700, or 800 is a reasonable prediction of the population at Midtown Junior High in 2006.

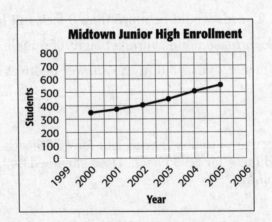

4. **FOOTBALL** In 2004, 565,192 people attended the Houston Texans 8 home games. Which is more reasonable for the number of people that attended each game: 60,000, 70,000, or 80,000?

3-10 Practice

Problem-Solving Investigation: Reasonable Answers

Mixed Problem Solving

Use the determine reasonable answers strategy to solve Exercises 1 and 2.

1. **LIFE EXPECTANCY** Use the graph below to determine whether 80, 85, or 90 years is a reasonable prediction of the life expectancy of a person born in 2020.

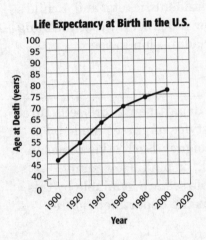

Life Expectancy at Birth in the U.S.

2. **SNACKS** Paolo is stocking up on after-school snacks. He wants to buy 2 pounds of bananas at $0.79 per pound, 2 cans of mixed nuts at $3.89 a can, and a bottle of apple juice at $1.19 a bottle. Does he need to bring $20 to the store or will $15 be enough? Explain your reasoning.

Use any strategy to solve Exercises 3–6. Some strategies are shown below.

Problem-Solving Strategies
• Solve a simpler problem.
• Draw a diagram.
• Determine reasonable answers.

3. **CARVINGS** In how many ways can Kwan line up her carvings of a duck, a gull, and a pelican on a shelf?

4. **CARNIVAL** There are 56 students in the sixth grade. Ms. Rockwell's class is sponsoring a carnival for the sixth graders at the school. The class has spent $40 on decorations and $10 on publicity. To pay for the expenses, an entrance fee of $0.75 is being considered. Is this a reasonable amount to charge?

5. **PARKS** The four largest national parks in the United States are in Alaska. The largest is Wrangell-St. Elias at 8.3 million acres. The fourth largest is Katmai at 1.48 million acres. How many times larger is Wrangell-St. Elias than Katmai to the nearest tenth million?

6. **RACING** Hector ran in the city charity race for four years. His times in minutes were: 14.8, 22.3, 26.7, and 31.9. What was his mean time for the four years to the nearest tenth minute?

Lesson 3-10

3-10 Word Problem Practice

Problem-Solving Investigation: Reasonable Answers

1. FOOD Anoki is selling cotton candy at the school carnival. The machine holds enough for 16 cotton candy treats. If he needs to refill the machine every 30 minutes, how many cotton candy treats can he expect to sell in 3 hours?

2. ZOOS The table shows the admission price to a local zoo.

Ticket Prices	
Adult	$7.00
Student	$4.50
Child under 5	$3.00

The Jung family is buying 2 adult tickets, 2 student tickets, and 1 child's ticket. How much will it cost the Jung family for admission to the zoo?

3. AGES Ava's mother is 3 times as old as Ava. Her grandmother is twice as old as Ava's mother. The sum of their three ages is 120. How old is Ava, her mother, and her grandmother?

4. PURSES A department store sells three different styles of purses made by a certain designer. Each style comes in navy, black, or pink. How many different purses are available by this designer at the department store?

5. FOOD Keegan stopped by the deli for his mom. If he has $14, does he have enough money to buy 1 pound of turkey, 1 pound of roast beef, and 1 pound of ham? Explain.

Lunch Meat Prices (lb)	
Ham	$3.95
Roast beef	$6.29
Salami	$2.99
Turkey	$2.99

6. PATTERNS Draw the next two figures in the pattern shown below.

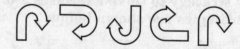

3 Student Recording Sheet

Use this recording sheet with pages 192–193 of the Student Edition.

Part 1: Multiple Choice

Read each question. Then fill in the correct answer.

1. Ⓐ Ⓑ Ⓒ Ⓓ

2. Ⓕ Ⓖ Ⓗ Ⓙ

3. Ⓐ Ⓑ Ⓒ Ⓓ

4. Ⓕ Ⓖ Ⓗ Ⓙ

5. Ⓐ Ⓑ Ⓒ Ⓓ

6. Ⓕ Ⓖ Ⓗ Ⓙ

7. Ⓐ Ⓑ Ⓒ Ⓓ

8. Ⓕ Ⓖ Ⓗ Ⓙ

9. Ⓐ Ⓑ Ⓒ Ⓓ

Part 2: Short Response/Grid in

Record your answer in the blank.

10. _____

11. _____

Part 3: Extended Response

Record your answers for Question 12 on the back of this paper.

Assessment

3 Rubric for Scoring Extended Response

(Use to score the Extended-Response question on page 193 of the Student Edition.)

General Scoring Guidelines

- If a student gives only a correct numerical answer to a problem but does not show how he or she arrived at the answer, the student will be awarded only 1 credit. All extended response questions require the student to show work.

- A fully correct answer for a multiple-part question requires correct responses for all parts of the question. For example, if a question has three parts, the correct response to one or two parts of the question that required work to be shown is *not* considered a fully correct response.

- Students who use trial and error to solve a problem must show their method. Merely showing that the answer checks or is correct is not considered a complete response for full credit.

Exercise 12 Rubric

Score	Specific Criteria
4	The sale price of each items is added to determine the total cost of the items as $63.50. The value is subtracted from the total original cost of the items to determine that she saved $19.45. The explanation of the savings is determined is correct and complete.
3	The values are correctly computed. However, the explanation is correct but not complete. **OR** The explanation is complete and correct, but one computational error is made in determining the values.
2	The values are correctly computed, but the explanation is incorrect or not given.
1	The explanation is incorrect or not given and only one of the two values is correct.
0	Response is completely incorrect.

3 **Chapter 3 Quiz 1**

SCORE _____

(Lessons 3-1 through 3-3)

For Questions 1–2, write each decimal in word form.

1. 0.6   2. 0.36

1. _____

2. _____

3. Write $(6 \times 1) + (2 \times 0.1) + (9 \times 0.01)$ in standard form.

3. _____

4. Write *four and twenty-three thousandths* in standard form.

4. _____

5. Use <, >, or = to compare the pair of decimals.
   2.016 ● 2.011.

5. _____

6. Order 18, 17.451, 18.45, 17.45 from least to greatest.

6. _____

For Questions 7–10, round each decimal to the indicated place-value position.

7. 23.971; tenths

7. _____

8. 47.825; hundredths

8. _____

9. 2.0124; thousandths

9. _____

10. 125.31; tens

10. _____

---

3 **Chapter 3 Quiz 2**

SCORE _____

(Lessons 3-4 and 3-5)

For Questions 1–4, round each decimal to the indicated place-value position.

1. 23.971; tenths

1. _____

2. 47.825; hundredths

2. _____

3. 2.0124; thousandths

3. _____

4. 125.3; tens

4. _____

5. **FOOD** A basket of fresh blackberries costs $3.49 at one grocery store. What is the price to the nearest dollar?

5. _____

Evaluate each expression if $a = 3.45$ and $b = 15.356$.

6. _____

6. $b - a$ 7. $a + b + 5$

7. _____

Assessment

3 Chapter 3 Quiz 3

(Lessons 3-6 and 3-7)

Multiply.

1. 1.2×6

2. 2.5×4

3. 3.1×5

4. 4.2×6

5. **GROCERIES** An orange cost $0.25 each. How much will 7 oranges cost?

6. 3.02×2.4

7. 0.65×0.25

8. **GIFT WRAP** A piece of gift wrap is 5.5 inches by 2.1 inches. What is the area of the gift wrap (multiply 5.5 and 2.1)?

1. _____

2. _____

3. _____

4. _____

5. _____

6. _____

7. _____

8. _____

---

3 Chapter 3 Quiz 4

(Lessons 3-8 through 3-10)

1. **ALGEBRA** Which of the three numbers 8.1, 8.3, 8.5 is the correct solution of $3.75t = 31.125$?

1. _____

Divide. Round to the nearest tenth if necessary.

2. $15.7 \div 3$

3. $85.375 \div 22$

4. **MEASUREMENT** The Akashi Kaikyo bridge in Japan has a main span of 6,532 feet. How many semi trailers could you line up along this span if the average length of the trailers is 40 feet 6 inches?

5. There are 28 students in the choir. If the number of students in the school is 4 times this amount, would about 80, 120, 160, or 200 be a reasonable estimate for the number of students in the school?

2. _____

3. _____

4. _____

5. _____

3 | **Chapter 3 Mid-Chapter Test**
(Lessons 3-1 through 3-5)

PART I

Write the letter for the correct answer in the blank at the right of each question.

1. Which number is greater than 8.042?
   A. 8.0420   B. 8.041   C. 8.0402   D. 8.42   1. _____

2. Which number is equal to 17.75?
   F. 1.775   G. 17.075   H. 17.750   I. 1.7750   2. _____

Round each decimal to the indicated place-value position.

3. 8.658; tenths
   A. 9.0   B. 8.7   C. 8.6   D. 8.66   3. _____

4. 18.475; ones
   F. 18   G. 18.5   H. 19   I. 20.0   4. _____

5. Estimate using rounding: 25.4 + 12.6.
   A. 38   B. 39   C. 30   D. 0   5. _____

PART II

GASOLINE For Questions 6 and 7, refer to the table at the right that shows the price per gallon of gas at four gas stations.

Station	Price
Gas-n-Go	$2.299
Flying J	$2.279
Fill-R-Up	$2.259
Gas for U	$2.289

6. Rita's dad always goes to the station with the cheapest price. Which station does he go to for gas?

6. _____

7. Round the Gas-n-Go price to the nearest cent.   7. _____

8. Order 13, 12.353, 13.351, and 12.35 from greatest to least.   8. _____

9. Write 8.034 in word form.   9. _____

10. Write $(6 \times 10) + (3 \times 1) + (1 \times 0.1) + (4 \times 0.01)$ in standard form.   10. _____

Find each sum or difference.

11. 12.45 + 17.55   11. _____

12. 17.89 + 12.55   12. _____

Assessment

3 Chapter 3 Vocabulary Test

| clustering | expanded form | standard form |
| equivalent decimals | front-end estimation | |

**Choose from the terms above to complete each sentence.
You will use each term more than once.**

1. When you estimate a sum or difference by adding or
   subtracting the front digits and then the next digits,
   you are using _____.

   1. _____

2. The _____ is the usual way in which we write
   decimals and other numbers.

   2. _____

3. Estimating by rounding a group of closely related
   numbers to the same number is called _____.

   3. _____

4. Decimals that name the same number are called
   _____.

   4. _____

5. The _____ is a way of writing decimals that uses
   the sum of the products of each digit and its place value.

   5. _____

6. 0.6 and 0.60 are examples of _____.

   6. _____

7. Writing decimals in the form 0.85 and 1.56 is an example
   of _____.

   7. _____

8. In the expression 34.6 + 52.3, adding first the 3 and 5
   and then the 4 and 2 and using a zero for the 6 and 3,
   is an example of _____.

   8. _____

9. Estimating by rounding 57.7, 61.1, 63.0, and 59.6 to 60.0
   is an example of _____.

   9. _____

10. Writing decimals in the form $(2 \times 1) + (8 \times 0.1) +$
    (5×0.01) is an example of _____.

    10. _____

Define each term in your own words.

11. decimal

    11. _____

12. decimal point

    12. _____

3 **Chapter 3 Test, Form 1**

SCORE _____

Write the letter for the correct answer in the blank at the right of each question.

1. Write 2.15 in word form.
   A. two fifteen
   C. two and fifteen thousandths
   B. two and fifteen hundredths
   D. two and fifteen two-thousandths

   1. _____

2. Write *four and twelve hundredths* in standard form.
   F. 4.12   G. 4.012   H. 0.0412   J. 0.412

   2. _____

3. Which number is less than 2.5?
   A. 5.2   B. 2.50   C. 2.05   D. 2.6

   3. _____

4. Order 5, 4.2, 5.02, and 4.3 from least to greatest.
   F. 5.02, 5, 4.3, 4.2
   H. 4.2, 4.3, 5, 5.02
   G. 4.3, 4.2, 5, 5.02
   J. 5.02, 4.2, 4.3, 5

   4. _____

5. Round 3.25 to the nearest tenth.
   A. 3.0   B. 3.2   C. 3.3   D. 4.0

   5. _____

6. Round 202.339 to the nearest hundredth.
   F. 200   G. 202   H. 202.34   J. 202.3

   6. _____

For Question 7 estimate using rounding.

7. **RESTAURANTS** Eddie orders one $4.25 ham sandwich and one $1.95 large orange juice. About how much is his meal?
   A. $4.00   B. $5.00   C. $6.00   D. $7.00

   7. _____

For Question 8, estimate using front-end estimation.

8. About how much more is $22.15 than $12.49?
   F. $20.00   G. $10.00   H. $8.00   J. $34.00

   8. _____

9. **TRAVEL** Maria's family went on a biking trip for four days. The table shows how many miles they traveled each day. Use clustering to estimate the total number of miles they rode on their trip.

Day	Miles
Sunday	26.5
Monday	25.1
Tuesday	25.6
Wednesday	24.8

   A. 75 miles   C. 100 miles
   B. 80 miles   D. 125 miles

   9. _____

For Questions 10 and 11, add or subtract.

10.   2.5
       + 1.3

   F. 1.2   G. 3.0   H. 4.0   J. 3.8

   10. _____

Assessment

11.   6.5
      − 2.4

   A. 4   **B.** 4.1   **C.** 5   **D.** 8.9   **11.** _____

12. ALGEBRA Evaluate $a + b$ if $a = 16.5$ and $b = 3.1$.

   F. 13.4   **G.** 19.0   **H.** 19.6   **J.** 20.0   **12.** _____

13. NUMBER SENSE A number is divided by 3. Then 8 is added to the quotient. After subtracting 5, the result is 7. What is the number?

   A. 9   **B.** 12   **C.** 15   **D.** 21   **13.** _____

Write the letter for the correct answer in the blank at the right of each question.

14. Evaluate $a \div b$ if $a = 4.4$ and $b = 2$.

   F. 8.8   **G.** 2.4   **H.** 2.2   **J.** 22   **14.** _____

15. Multiply 1.2 and t if $t = 3.4$.

   A. 0.408   **B.** 408   **C.** 40.8   **D.** 4.08   **15.** _____

16. Find the area of the rectangle.

   F. 322 ft^2 **H.** 48.4 ft^2

   G. 4.84 ft^2 **J.** 32.2 ft^2

12.1 ft   4 ft   **16.** _____

17. Find $19.6 \div 7$.

   A. 28   **B.** 280   **C.** 2.8   **D.** 0.28   **17.** _____

18. Find $2.736 \div 0.9$.

   F. 34   **G.** 3.4   **H.** 30.4   **J.** 3.04   **18.** _____

19. Divide. Round to the nearest tenth: $10.5\overline{)5.45}$.

   A. 0.5   **B.** 0.52   **C.** 5.2   **D.** 0.519   **19** _____

20. Evaluate $40.6 \div y$ if $y = 20$.

   F. 20.3   **G.** 2.03   **H.** 203   **J.** 0.203   **20.** _____

Bonus PAYMENTS Rina is making payments of $39.50 per month for 18 months for her new stereo. How much will she pay in all?   **B:** _____

3 **Chapter 3 Test, Form 2A**

Write the letter for the correct answer in the blank at the right of each question.

1. Write *twenty and fifteen hundredths* in standard form.
   A. 20.15
   B. 20.015
   C. 0.2015
   D. 0.215

   1. _____

2. Write *two and thirteen hundredths* in expanded form.
   F. (213×0.001)
   G. $(2 \times 0.1) + (1 \times 0.1) + (3 \times 0.1)$
   H. $(2 \times 1) + (13 \times 0.001)$
   J. $(2 \times 1) + (1 \times 0.1) + (3 \times 0.01)$

   2. _____

3. Which number is less than 2.06?
   A. 6.02
   B. 2.6
   C. 2.060
   D. 2.006

   3. _____

4. Order 19, 18.2, 19.03, and 18.231 from greatest to least.
   F. 18.231, 18.2, 19, 19.03
   G. 19.03, 19, 18.231, 18.2
   H. 19.03, 19, 18.2, 18.231
   J. 19, 18.2, 19.03, 18.231

   4. _____

Round the decimal to the indicated place-value position.

5. 112.363; hundredths
   A. 112
   B. 112.4
   C. 112.37
   D. 112.36

   5. _____

For Questions 6–7, estimate using rounding.

6. $3.8 + 4.05 + 4.7$
   F. 13
   G. 12.50
   H. 12
   J. 11

   6. _____

7. **RESTAURANTS** Somwa orders a $4.79 chicken sandwich, a $2.89 side of macaroni salad, and $1.49 large ice tea. About how much is her meal?
   A. $7.00
   B. $9.00
   C. $8.00
   D. $8.50

   7. _____

For Questions 8, estimate using front-end estimation.

8. 65.05
   + 13.55

   F. 70.00
   G. 51.00
   H. 78.55
   J. 78.00

   8. _____

For Questions 9 and 10, add or subtract.

9. 17.3
   + 2.4

   A. 19.0
   B. 14.9
   C. 19.7
   D. 20

   9. _____

10. 19.25
   − 2.64

   F. 17.00
   G. 1.661
   H. 16.61
   J. 21.89

   10. _____

Assessment

WEATHER For Questions 11 and 12, refer to the table that shows average rainfall for Hilo, Hawaii.

Month	Inches
July	9.71
Aug.	9.34
Sept.	8.53
Oct.	9.6

11. Use clustering to find an estimate for the total rainfall for the four months shown.

   A. 27 inches   **C.** 38 inches

   B. 36 inches   **D.** 35 inches

   11. _____

12. Find the actual total rainfall for the four months shown.

   F. 27.58 inches   **G.** 36.58 inches   **H.** 37.18 inches   **J.** 38.66 inches   12. _____

13. **ALGEBRA** Evaluate $b - a$ if $a = 2.45$ and $b = 36.356$.

   A. 33.906   **B.** 11.856   **C.** 38.806   **D.** 34.000   13. _____

14. **TIME** After Chantel woke up, she got ready for school for 45 minutes, finished her homework for 15 minutes, and then it took her 30 minutes to get to school. If it is now 7:45 A.M., what time did Chantel wake up in the morning?

   F. 5:45 A.M.   **G.** 6:00 A.M.   **H.** 6:15 A.M.   **J.** 6:30 A.M.   14. _____

Write the letter for the correct answer in the blank at the right of each question.

15. Find 21.4×3.8.

   A. 8.132   **B.** 813.2   **C.** 81.32   **D.** 0.8132   15. _____

16. Find $\$3.12 \times 86$.

   F. $24.35   **G.** $26.83   **H.** $243.51   **J.** $268.32   16. _____

17. Find the area of the rectangle.

   A. 4.11 in²   **C.** 41.1 in²

   B. 33.4 in²   **D.** 16.7 in²

   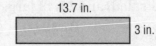
   13.7 in.   3 in.

   17. _____

18. Find $110.92 \div 47$.

   F. 2.36   **G.** 23.6   **H.** 0.236   **J.** 236   18. _____

19. Find $11.52 \div 0.72$.

   A. 16   **B.** 1.6   **C.** 0.16   **D.** 0.016   19. _____

20. Evaluate $104.5 \div t$ if $t = 38$.

   F. 0.275   **G.** 2.75   **H.** 27.5   **J.** 275   20. _____

3 Chapter 3 Test, Form 2B

Write the letter for the correct answer in the blank at the right of each question.

1. Write *thirty and seventeen hundredths* in standard form.
   A. 30.017   **B.** 30.17   **C.** 0.317   **D.** 0.3017   1. _____

2. Write *three and fourteen hundredths* in expanded form.
   F. $(3 \times 0.1) + (1 \times 0.1) + (4 \times 0.1)$ **H.** $(3 \times 1) + (1 \times 0.1) + (4 \times 0.01)$
   G. $(3 \times 1) + (14 \times 0.001)$ **J.** (314×0.001) 2. _____

3. Which number is less than 3.07?
   A. 7.03   **B.** 3.7   **C.** 3.070   **D.** 3.007   3. _____

4. Order 17, 16.2, 17.02, and 16.471 from greatest to least.
   F. 17.02, 17, 16.471, 16.2   **H.** 17.02, 17, 16.2, 16.471
   G. 16.471, 16.2, 17, 17.02   **J.** 17, 16.2, 17.02, 16.471   4. _____

For Question 5, round each decimal to the indicated place-value position.

5. 116.563; hundredths
   A. 116   **B.** 116.56   **C.** 116.57   **D.** 116.6   5. _____

For Questions 6, estimate using rounding.

6. 4.7 + 5.07 + 5.8
   F. 15.5   **G.** 16   **H.** 15   **J.** 14   6. _____

7. **RESTAURANTS** Vashti orders a $3.59 tuna sandwich, a $1.89 side of potato salad, and $1.29 large orange juice. About how much is her meal?
   A. $6.50   **B.** $9.00   **C.** $8.00   **D.** $7.00   7. _____

For Question 8, estimate using front-end estimation.

8.   34.05
   + 12.65

   F. 46.00   **G.** 47.00   **H.** 46.70   **J.** 22.00   8. _____

For Questions 9 and 10, add or subtract.

9.   16.3
   + 3.2

   A. 13.1   **B.** 19.5   **C.** 20   **D.** 19.0   9. _____

10.   18.25
   − 2.43

   F. 15.82   **G.** 20.68   **H.** 16.00   **J.** 1.582   10. _____

Assessment

3 ## Chapter 3 Test, Form 2B *(continued)*

WEATHER **For Questions 11 and 12, refer to the table that shows the average rainfall for Vero Beach, Florida.**

Month	Inches
June	6.46
July	6.09
Aug.	6.1
Sept.	7.15

11. Use clustering to find an estimate for the total rainfall for the four months shown.

  A. 18 inches   **C.** 24 inches

  B. 20 inches   **D.** 25 inches   11. _____

12. Find the actual total rainfall for the four months shown.

  F. 19.70 inches   **G.** 20.31 inches   **H.** 25.70 inches   **J.** 25.80 inches   12. _____

13. **ALGEBRA** Evaluate $b - a$ if $a = 2.35$ and $b = 36.258$.

  A. 38.608   **B.** 15.242   **C.** 34.000   **D.** 33.908   13. _____

14. **TIME** After school, Pedro rode his bike for 15 minutes, played with his friends for 45 minutes, and studied for an hour. If it is now 5:30 P.M., what time did Pedro get home from school?

  F. 3:30 P.M.   **G.** 3:45 P.M.   **H.** 4:00 P.M.   **J.** 4:15 P.M.   14. _____

Write the letter for the correct answer in the blank at the right of each question.

15. Find 31.6×4.2.

  A. 13.272   **B.** 132.72   **C.** 1.3272   **D.** 1327.2   15. _____

16. Find $\$3.06 \times 48$.

  F. $14.69   **G.** $1,468.80   **H.** $146.88   **J.** $14,688   16. _____

17. Find the area of the rectangle.

  A. 45.8 sq m   **C.** 22.9 sq m

  B. 75.6 sq m   **D.** 7.56 sq m

  18.9 m

  4 m

  17. _____

18. Find $47.6 \div 34$.

  F. 14   **G.** 140   **H.** 0.14   **J.** 1.4   18. _____

19. Find $4.944 \div 1.6$.

  A. 3.09   **B.** 3.9   **C.** 30.9   **D.** 39   19. _____

20. Evaluate $204.96 \div s$ if $s = 12$.

  F. 170.8   **G.** 17.08   **H.** 1,708   **J.** 1.708   20. _____

Bonus MONEY Oliver bought 13 gallons of gasoline for $28.34. How much did each gallon of gasoline cost?   **B:** _____

3 **Chapter 3 Test, Form 2C** SCORE _____

For Questions 1–2, write each decimal in word form.

1. 7.26

1. _____

2. 15.731

2. _____

3. Write *forty-seven and fifteen hundredths* in standard form.

3. _____

4. Write *forty-seven and fifteen hundredths* in expanded form.

4. _____

For Questions 5 and 6 use >, <, or = to compare each pair of decimals.

5. 2.001 ● 2.01

5. _____

6. 87.02 ● 86.025

6. _____

7. Order 16.851, 15.852, 16.1, 15.802 from least to greatest.

7. _____

For Questions 8–9, round each decimal to the indicated place-value position.

8. 5.345; tenths

8. _____

9. 12.536; ones

9. _____

10. **ENERGY** An electric company charges $0.138295 per kilowatt hour of electricity used. Round $0.138295 to the nearest cent.

10. _____

For Question 11, estimate using rounding.

11. 5.3 + 6.08 + 8.7

11. _____

12. **FOOD** Anita orders one $4.89 dish of chicken chow mein, one $2.69 bowl of miso soup, and one $1.49 side order of steamed rice. Estimate the price of her meal.

12. _____

For Questions 13 and 14, estimate using front-end estimation.

13. 78.35
    − 13.51

14. 16.55
    + 12.92

13. _____

14. _____

Add or subtract.

15. 8.3
    + 2.6

16. 18.75
    − 3.92

15. _____

16. _____

17. 0.078 + 42.35 + 0.2

17. _____

18. **WOODWORKING** Tanya is making a doll house for her sister. One piece of wood is 11.5 inches long. If she uses 6.75 inches for the window sill, how much does she have left for the welcome sign?

18. _____

Assessment

3 Chapter 3 Test, Form 2C *(continued)*

ALGEBRA Evaluate each expression if $a = 4.95$ and $b = 16.775$.

19. $b - a$

20. $9 + a + b$

19. _____

20. _____

WEATHER For Questions 21–22, refer to the table at the right that shows the average monthly rainfall for New Orleans, Louisiana.

Month	Inches
Jan.	5.12
Feb.	6.00
Mar.	5.00
Apr.	4.51

21. Use clustering to estimate the total rainfall for the four months shown.

21. _____

22. Find the actual total rainfall for the four months shown.

22. _____

Multiply.

23. 38.4×5.7

23. _____

24. 0.89×48

24. _____

25. 3.61×3.61

25. _____

26. 428×1.32

26. _____

Find the area of each rectangle.

27.

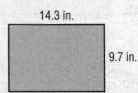

2.5 yd

5 yd

27. _____

28.

14.3 in.

9.7 in.

28. _____

Divide.

29. $75.6 \div 42$

29. _____

30. $3.822 \div 0.49$

30. _____

31. $273.6 \div 3.6$

31. _____

32. $296.805 \div 42.1$

32. _____

33. SHARING If 4 people are going to share 14.8 ounces of cheese, how much will each person get?

33. _____

Bonus **SHOPPING** Tai buys three gifts for his family that cost $12.99, $7.10, and $8.05, including tax. Tai gives the sales clerk $30. How much change should he get back?

B: _____

3 **Chapter 3 Test, Form 2D**

For Questions 1–2, write each decimal in word form.

1. 0.4

2. 13.651

3. Write *thirty-two and fourteen hundredths* in standard form.

4. Write *thirty-two and fourteen hundredths* in expanded form.

For Questions 5 and 6 use >, <, or = to compare each pair of decimals.

5. 4.02 ● 4.002   6. 67.021 ● 68.02

7. Order 19.44, 18.951, 19.1, 18.901 from least to greatest.

For Questions 8 and 9, round each decimal to the indicated place-value position.

8. 7.275; tenths

9. 48.799; hundredths

10. **ENERGY** An electric company charges $0.13371 per kilowatt hour of electricity used. Round $0.13371 to the nearest cent.

For Question 11, estimate using rounding.

11. 4.3 + 5.09 + 7.7

12. **FOOD** Juan orders one $3.69 hamburger, one $2.89 side order of potato salad, and one $1.19 large milk. Estimate the price of his meal.

For Questions 13 and 14, estimate using front-end estimation.

13. 67.23
   − 15.54

14. 14.58
   + 12.84

Add or subtract.

15. 7.4
   + 3.3

16. 17.25
   − 2.72

17. 38.16 + 0.091 + 0.4

18. **WOODWORKING** Alexa is making a model train station for her brother. One piece of wood is 13.5 inches long. If she uses 11.75 inches for the fence, how much does she have left for the railroad crossing sign?

1. _____ 2. _____ 3. _____ 4. _____ 5. _____ 6. _____ 7. _____ 8. _____ 9. _____ 10. _____ 11. _____ 12. _____ 13. _____ 14. _____ 15. _____ 16. _____ 17. _____ 18. _____

Assessment

ALGEBRA Evaluate each expression if $a = 3.95$ and $b = 17.885$.

19. $b - a$ 20. $6 + a + b$

19. _____

20. _____

WEATHER For Questions 21 and 22, refer to the table at the right that shows the average monthly rainfall for Quillayute, Washington.

Month	Inches
July	3.12
Aug.	2.57
Sept.	2.54
Oct.	4.88

21. Use clustering to estimate the total rainfall for the four months shown.

21. _____

22. Find the actual total rainfall for the four months shown.

22. _____

Multiply.

23. 8.6×4.9

23. _____

24. 0.72×26

24. _____

25. 8.97×6.8

25. _____

26. 136×4.32

26. _____

Find the area of each rectangle.

27.

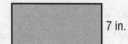

3.5 in.

7 in.

27. _____

28.

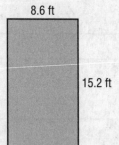

8.6 ft

15.2 ft

28. _____

Divide.

29. $231.68 \div 32$

29. _____

30. $19.98 \div 0.74$

30. _____

31. $48.97 \div 5.9$

31. _____

32. $73.923 \div 12.3$

32. _____

33. SHARING If 5 people are going to share 34.5 ounces of peanuts, how much will each person get?

33. _____

Bonus SHOPPING Fiona buys three shirts that cost $8.99, $13.05, and $6.10, including tax. Fiona gives the sales clerk $30. How much change should she get back?

B: _____

3 Chapter 3 Test, Form 3

For Questions 1–2, write each decimal in word form.

1. 0.0026

2. 212.03

3. Write *ninety-six thousandths* in standard form.

4. Write $(3 \times 0.1) + (4 \times 0.01)$ in word form.

For Questions 5 and 6 use >, <, or =, to compare each pair of decimals.

5. 4.0022 ● 4.021

6. 88.02 ● 87.021

7. Order 35.1035, 35.935, 35.036, and 3.99 from greatest to least.

For Questions 8–9, round each decimal to the indicated place-value position.

8. 6.951; tenths

9. 512.536; ones

10. **SHOPPING** A pair of shoes costs $29.99 plus $2.3992 sales tax. Round the sales tax to the nearest cent. Then find the total cost of the shoes.

For Questions 11–12, estimate using rounding.

11. 5.3 + 6.08 + 8.721 + 8.9

12. 2.5353 − 0.44

13. **FOOD** Kim orders one $2.89 salad, one $2.69 bowl of soup, one $1.49 side order of garlic bread, and one $1.19 milk. Estimate the price of her meal.

For Questions 14, estimate using front-end estimation.

14. 21.55
    + 12.91

Add or subtract.

15. 9.68
    + 4

16. 9.7 − 8.359

17. **GASOLINE** In January 2006, the average price per gallon of gas on the West Coast was $2.372, while on the East Coast it was $2.381. Which one was closer to the national average of $2.320? How close was it?

18. **CONSTRUCTION** Sam is building a treehouse out of scrap wood. One piece of wood is 12 feet long. If he uses 6.5 feet for part of the floor and 4.125 feet for the side railing, how much is left for the "Keep Out" sign?

1. _____

2. _____

3. _____

4. _____

5. _____

6. _____

7. _____

8. _____

9. _____

10. _____

11. _____

12. _____

13. _____

14. _____

15. _____

16. _____

17. _____

18. _____

Assessment

COMPUTERS For Questions 19–20, refer to the table at the right that shows the file sizes for five digital pictures.

Picture	File Size (megabytes)
Birthday	0.8
Best Friends	0.9
Waterfall	1.7
Soccer Team	1.4
Camping	2.1

19. Use front-end estimation to estimate the sum of the file sizes.

19. _____

20. There is 20 megabytes of free space left on a compact disc. How many megabytes of free space will be left after the five files are saved to the disc?

20. _____

Evaluate each expression if $a = 3.35$ and $b = 15.858$.

21. $b - a$

22. $a + 2.7 + b$

21. _____

22. _____

23. **NUMBER SENSE** A number is multiplied by 11. Next, 125 is subtracted from the product. Then 28 is added to the difference. If the result is 90, what is the number?

23. _____

24. **HEIGHT** Eli is 1.5 inches taller than Bianca. Bianca is 0.5 inches shorter than Raul and 1 inch taller than Carly. Chi, who is 5 feet 4 inches tall, is 2.5 inches shorter than Eli. How tall is each student?

24. _____

25. Evaluate $f \div e$ if $e = 19$ and $f = 252.7$.

25. _____

26. Which of the numbers 3, 4, or 5 is the solution of $y \times 4.23 = 21.15$?

26. _____

Multiply.

27. 6.34×1.5

28. 3.99×24

27. _____

28. _____

Find the area of each figure.

29.

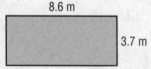
8.6 m
3.7 m

30.

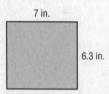
7 in.
6.3 in.

29. _____

30. _____

Divide.

31. $9.45 \div 7$

32. $3.3 \div 1.1$

31. _____

32. _____

Round to the nearest hundredth.

33. What is $8.24 \div 0.00032$?

33. _____

Bonus MONEY MATTERS Isidro wants to purchase a new scooter that costs $79.95. The sales tax is found by multiplying the price of the scooter by 0.065. Find the total amount of money Isidro will pay. Round to the nearest cent.

B: _____

3 Chapter 3 Extended-Response Test

Demonstrate your knowledge by giving a clear, concise solution to each problem. Be sure to include all relevant drawings and justify your answers. You may show your solution in more than one way or investigate beyond the requirements of the problem. If necessary, record your answer on another piece of paper.

1. Look at the chart of average body lengths of some Death Valley lizards.

Animals	Length (cm)
Western whiptail lizard	8.75
Western banded gecko	7
Desert horned lizard	8.25
Gilbert's skink	8.3

   a. Put the lengths in the table in order from greatest to least. Explain your steps.

   b. A chuckwalla lizard has an average body length of 17.145 centimeters. Explain how to round 17.145 to the nearest hundredth. Then use your rounded decimal to find the difference in length between the chuckwalla and the Gilbert's skink.

2. Use the rainfall information to answer the questions.

Death Valley Average Rainfall (millimeters)			
Summer Season		Winter Season	
May	1.77	November	4.8
June	0.8	December	4.75
July	2.8	January	6
August	3	February	8.4

   a. Estimate the total rainfall for each season. Explain your method.
   b. Find the actual total rainfall for each season. Explain your steps.
   c. Which season has more total rainfall? How much more? Explain how you determined this.

3. TIME After school let out, Taryn spent 30 minutes on homework. Then she had volleyball practice for one and a half hours. After practice, it took Taryn 15 minutes to walk home from school. It is now 4:45 P.M.

   a. What time did volleyball practice get over?
   b. What time did volleyball practice start?
   c. What time did school let out?

4. The people of a neighborhood are creating a large community vegetable and fruit garden.

   a. One part of the garden will have 6 rows of corn plants. Each row will be 11.25 feet long. Irrigation soaker hoses will be laid along each row of corn plants. How many feet of soaker hose will be needed? Explain the steps you went through to solve this problem. Be sure to explain how you decided where to place the decimal point.

   b. The neighbors have $18.57 to spend on strawberry plants. A 6-pack of plants costs $2. How many packs can they buy? Show your work.

Assessment

3 · Standardized Test Practice

(Chapters 1–3)

Part 1: Multiple Choice

Instructions: Fill in the appropriate circle for the best answer.

1. What is the prime factorization of 40? (Lesson 1-2)

   A 1×40 **C** $2 \times 2 \times 2 \times 5$

   B $2 \times 4 \times 5$ **D** 4×10 1. Ⓐ Ⓑ Ⓒ Ⓓ

2. Find the value of $21 + 3^3 \div 3$. (Lesson 1-4)

   F 34   **G** 16   **H** 22   **J** 30   2. Ⓕ Ⓖ Ⓗ Ⓙ

3. Evaluate $4y \div 3$ if $y = 9$. (Lesson 1-5)

   A 3   **B** 6   **C** 9   **D** 12   3. Ⓐ Ⓑ Ⓒ Ⓓ

4. In the bar graph showing the number of books read, what is the interval for the data? (Lesson 2-2)

   F 25   **H** 10

   G 20   **J** 5   4. Ⓕ Ⓖ Ⓗ Ⓙ

   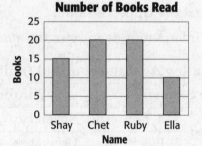

   Number of Books Read

5. One store sells skateboards for $59.35, $65.45, and $85.20. What is the mean price of a skateboard at the store? (Lesson 2-6)

   A $60.00   **B** $65.45   **C** $70.00   **D** $75.00   5. Ⓐ Ⓑ Ⓒ Ⓓ

6. Which of the following data sets has the greatest range? (Lesson 2-7)

   F {15, 3, 12}   **H** {1021, 1023}

   G {31, 35, 34}   **J** {4, 5, 6, 7}   6. Ⓕ Ⓖ Ⓗ Ⓙ

7. Which measure of central tendency is most misleading for the temperature data 66°, 60°, 70°, 72°, 60°, 68°? (Lesson 2-8)

   A mean   **B** mode   **C** interval   **D** median   7. Ⓐ Ⓑ Ⓒ Ⓓ

8. Write *twenty-three and sixteen hundredths* in standard form. (Lesson 3-1)

   F 23,160   **G** 23.16   **H** 23.016   **J** 23.0016   8. Ⓕ Ⓖ Ⓗ Ⓙ

9. Write *six and fifty-two hundredths* in expanded form. (Lesson 3-1)

   A 6.52   **C** $(6 \times 1) + (52 \times 0.01)$

   B 6.052   **D** $(6 \times 1) + (5 \times 0.1) + (2 \times 0.01)$ 9. Ⓐ Ⓑ Ⓒ Ⓓ

10. Which decimal is least? (Lesson 3-2)

    F 4.05   **G** 4.052   **H** 4.1   **J** 4.001   10. Ⓕ Ⓖ Ⓗ Ⓙ

3 **Standardized Test Practice** *(continued)*

(Chapters 1–3)

11. Order 12.02, 11.5, 12, 11.695 from least to greatest. (Lesson 3-2)

    A 11.5, 11.695, 12.02, 12   **B** 12.02, 12, 11.5, 11.695

    C 11.695, 11.5, 12, 12.02   **D** 11.5, 11.695, 12, 12.02   **11.** Ⓐ Ⓑ Ⓒ Ⓓ

12. Round 2001.025 to the nearest hundredth. (Lesson 3-3)

    F 2001   **G** 2001.0   **H** 2001.02   **J** 2001.03   **12.** Ⓕ Ⓖ Ⓗ Ⓙ

13. Alaskan farmer John Evans holds the world record for a 19.985 pound carrot. Round 19.985 to the nearest tenth. (Lesson 3-3)

    A 19.0   **B** 19.98   **C** 19.99   **D** 20.0   **13.** Ⓐ Ⓑ Ⓒ Ⓓ

14. Use rounding to estimate 44.72 + 21.15. (Lesson 3-4)

    F 24   **G** 65   **H** 66   **J** 67   **14.** Ⓕ Ⓖ Ⓗ Ⓙ

15. What is 19.036 − 2.15? (Lesson 3-5)

    A 17.15   **B** 18.821   **C** 16.886   **D** 21.186   **15.** Ⓐ Ⓑ Ⓒ Ⓓ

16. Find 8 + 5.79. (Lesson 3-5)

    F 5.87   **G** 6.59   **H** 13.79   **J** 14.67   **16.** Ⓕ Ⓖ Ⓗ Ⓙ

17. Find $23.00 − 21.50. (Lesson 3-5)

    A $1.50   **B** $2.00   **C** $2.50   **D** $3.00   **17.** Ⓐ Ⓑ Ⓒ Ⓓ

18. Multiply 1.2×8.

    F 96   **G** 960   **H** 9.6   **J** 100   **18.** Ⓕ Ⓖ Ⓗ Ⓙ

19. Multiply 1.2×2.5

    A 300   **B** 30   **C** 3   **D** 0   **19.** Ⓐ Ⓑ Ⓒ Ⓓ

20. Divide $1.2 \div 6$.

    F 20   **G** 2   **H** 0.2   **J** 0.02   **20.** Ⓕ Ⓖ Ⓗ Ⓙ

21. Divide $0.72 \div 0.6$.

    A 1.2   **B** 12   **C** 120   **D** 1200   **21.** Ⓐ Ⓑ Ⓒ Ⓓ

22. Xing's room is 12.5 feet long. Her brother's room is 0.8 feet longer. Which is a reasonable estimate for the length of her brother's room?

    F 20.5 feet   **G** 4.5 feet   **H** 13.5 feet   **J** 16 feet   **22.** Ⓕ Ⓖ Ⓗ Ⓙ

Assessment

3 Standardized Test Practice (continued)

(Chapters 1–3)

Part 2: Short Response

Instructions: Write your answers to each question in the space provided.

---

23. What is the mean of the numbers 2.31, 1.6, and 2.09? (Lesson 2-6)

23. _____

24. Use rounding to the nearest whole number to estimate 24.3 + 4.9 + 2.089. (Lesson 3-4)

24. _____

25. Complete the pattern: 3, 4, 6, 9, ___, ___, ___. (Lesson 1-1)

25. _____

MONEY Vera earns $75, $90, $75, $82, and $98 the first five weeks at her summer job.

26. Make a line graph of Vera's earnings for the five weeks. (Lesson 2-2)

26.

27. What is the mean amount she earned per week? (Lesson 2-6)

27. _____

28. Which average is most misleading for the data? Why? (Lesson 2-8)

28. _____

29. Replace ● with >, <, or = to make 22.003 ● 22.033 a true sentence. (Lesson 3-2)

29. _____

30. ALGEBRA Evalute $b - a$ if $a = 4.776$ and $b = 13.8$. (Lesson 3-5)

30. _____

31. NUTRITION As part of a heart-healthy diet, Gina's dad is supposed to eat less than 23 grams of saturated fat per day. The table to the right shows his breakfast and lunch. (Lesson 3-5)

Food	Saturated Fat (grams)
Orange juice	0.1
Toast with butter	3.1
2 fried eggs	3.8
1% milk	1.5
Cheeseburger	15.1

  a. For breakfast he had juice, toast, and eggs. How many grams of saturated fat are in his breakfast?

  b. Will he be able to meet his goal if he eats a sensible dinner? Explain.

  c. Gina has just learned about different ways to estimate sums. If she's going to estimate here, why is rounding the best estimation strategy?

a. _____

b. _____

c. _____

---

3 Anticipation Guide

Adding and Subtracting Decimals

NAME _____ DATE _____ PERIOD _____

STEP 1 *Before you begin Chapter 3*

- Read each statement.
- Decide whether you Agree (A) or Disagree (D) with the statement.
- Write A or D in the first column OR if you are not sure whether you agree or disagree, write NS (Not Sure).

STEP 1 A, D, or NS	Statement	STEP 2 A or D
	1. The decimal 0.42 represents 42 hundredths.	A
	2. 0.70 is greater than 0.7 because 70 is greater than 7.	D
	3. On a number line, numbers to the right of zero are positive and numbers to the left of zero are negative.	A
	4. To round a decimal to the hundredths place, look at the digit in the thousandths place.	A
	5. The decimal 2.628 can be rounded to 2.63 or 2.6.	A
	6. To estimate the sum of two decimals, always round both decimals to the tenths place.	D
	7. Only decimals to the same place value can be added or subtracted.	D
	8. When solving math problems, estimation can be used when an exact answer is not necessary.	A
	9. To multiply a decimal by a whole number, you must first rewrite the whole number as a decimal.	D
	10. The solution to 3.5 × 4.62 will have three decimal places.	D
	11. Before dividing by a decimal, change the divisor to a whole number.	D

STEP 2 *After you complete Chapter 3*

- Reread each statement and complete the last column by entering an A (Agree) or a D (Disagree).
- Did any of your opinions about the statements change from the first column?
- For those statements that you mark with a D, use a separate sheet of paper to explain why you disagree. Use examples, if possible.

3-1 Lesson Reading Guide

Representing Decimals

NAME _____ DATE _____ PERIOD _____

Get Ready for the Lesson

Complete the Mini Lab at the top of page 138 in your textbook.

Model each decimal using a place-value chart, money, a decimal model, and base-ten blocks. **1–4 See students' work.**

1. 1.56

2. 0.85

3. 0.08

4. $2.25

Read the Lesson

5. What does the decimal point do? **It separates the whole number part of the decimal from the part that is less than one.**

6. How does changing the decimal point in 5.78 to 57.8 affect the value of the decimal? **It makes the value of the decimal tens times greater.**

Remember What You Learned

7. Look up the words *dime* and *decimal* in a dictionary. How is *dime* related to *decimal*? Explain how our money system (dollars, dimes, pennies) and the place-value chart use base ten. **Sample answer: Both come from the Latin word *decem*, which means ten. In our money system, 10 pennies have the same value as one dime, and 10 dimes have the same value as one dollar. So, one dollar has a value ten times greater than one dime, and one dime has a value ten times greater than one penny. In the place-value chart, as you go from one column to the next to the left, you multiply by 10. As you go to the right, you divide by 10.**

Answers (Lesson 3-1)

3-1 Skills Practice
Representing Decimals

Write each decimal in word form.

1. 6.5 **six and five tenths**
2. 0.3 **three tenths**
3. 39.2 **thirty-nine and two tenths**
4. 0.83 **eighty-three hundredths**
5. 5.67 **five and sixty-seven hundredths**
6. 14.006 **fourteen and six thousandths**
7. 12.001 **twelve and one thousandth**
8. 0.5214 **five thousand two hundred fourteen ten-thousandths**
9. 12.0905 **twelve and nine hundred five ten-thousandths**

Write each decimal in standard form and in expanded form.

10. three tenths **0.3; (3 × 0.1)**
11. fifteen and one tenth **15.1; (1 × 10) + (5 × 1) + (1 × 0.1)**
12. eight and four hundredths **8.04 (8 × 1) + (0 × 0.1) + (4 × 0.01)**
13. seventy-two and sixteen thousandths **72.016; (7 × 10) + (2 × 1) + (0 × 0.1) + (1 × 0.01) + (6 × 0.001)**
14. one hundred and one hundredth **100.01 (1 × 100) + (0 × 10) + (0 × 1) + (0 × 0.1) + (1 × 0.01)**
15. four hundred seven thousandths **0.407 (4 × 0.1) + (0 × 0.01) + (7 × 0.001)**
16. four hundred seven ten-thousandths **0.0407 (0 × 0.1) + (4 × 0.01) + (0 × 0.001) + (7 × 0.0001)**
17. one hundred and one thousandth **100.001 (1 × 100) + (0 × 10) + (0 × 1) + (0 × 0.1) + (0 × 0.01) + (1 × 0.001)**
18. Express (2 × 100) + (3 × 10) + (1 × 1) + (4 × 0.1) + (5 × 0.01) in word form. **two hundred thirty-one and forty-five hundredths**

Chapter 3   11   Course 1

3-1 Study Guide and Intervention
Representing Decimals

Decimals can be written in standard form and expanded form.

Standard form is the usual way to write a decimal, such as 3.52. **Expanded form** is a sum of the products of each digit and its place, such as (3 × 1) + (5 × 0.1) + (2 × 0.01).

Example 1 Write 128.0732 in word form.

Place-Value Chart

thousands	hundreds	tens	ones	tenths	hundredths	thousandths	ten-thousandths
0	1	2	8	0	7	3	2

In words, 128.0732 is *one hundred twenty-eight and seven hundred thirty-two ten-thousandths.*

Example 2 Write *ninety-nine and two hundred seven thousandths* in standard form and expanded form.

Place-Value Chart

thousands	hundreds	tens	ones	tenths	hundredths	thousandths	ten-thousandths
0	0	9	9	2	0	7	0

Standard form: 99.207
Expanded form: (9 × 10) + (9 × 1) + (2 × 0.1) + (0 × 0.01) + (7 × 0.001)

Exercises

Write each decimal in word form.

1. 2.3 **two and three tenths**
2. 0.68 **sixty-eight hundredths**
3. 32.501 **thirty-two and five hundred one thousandths**
4. 0.0036 **thirty-six ten-thousandths**

Write each decimal in standard form and in expanded form.

5. twenty and two hundredths **standard: 20.02; expanded: (2 × 10) + (0 × 1) + (0 × 0.1) + (2 × 0.01)**
6. seven and five tenths **standard: 7.5; expanded: (7 × 1) + (5 × 0.1)**
7. three hundred four ten-thousandths **standard: 0.0304; expanded: (0 × 0.1) + (3 × 0.01) + (0 × 0.001) + (4 × 0.0001)**
8. eleven thousandths **standard: 0.011; expanded: (0 × 0.1) + (1 × 0.01) + (1 × 0.001)**

Chapter 3   10   Course 1

Answers (Lesson 3-1)

Practice (page 12)

NAME _____ DATE _____ PERIOD _____

3-1 Practice

Representing Decimals

Write each decimal in word form.

1. 0.5
   five tenths

2. 0.1
   one tenth

3. 2.49
   two and forty-nine hundredths

4. 8.07
   eight and seven hundredths

5. 0.345
   three hundred forty-five thousandths

6. 30.089
   thirty and eighty-nine thousandths

7. 6.0735
   six and seven hundred thirty-five ten-thousandths

8. 0.0042
   forty-two ten-thousandths

9. 16.375
   sixteen and three hundred seventy-five thousandths

Write each decimal in standard form and in expanded form.

10. one tenth **0.1; 1×0.1**

11. thirteen and four tenths
    13.4; $(1 \times 10) + (3 \times 1) + (4 \times 0.1)$

12. sixty-two and thirty-five hundredths
    62.35; $(6 \times 10) + (2 \times 1) + (3 \times 0.1) + (5 \times 0.01)$

13. seven hundred twelve ten-thousandths
    0.0712; $(0 \times 0.1) + (7 \times 0.01) + (1 \times 0.001) + (2 \times 0.0001)$

14. How is 611.0079 written in word form?
    six hundred eleven and seventy-nine ten-thousandths

15. Write $(2 \times 0.1) + (8 \times 0.01)$ in word form. **twenty-eight hundredths**

16. Write $(5 \times 0.001) + (6 \times 0.0001)$ in standard form. **0.0056**

17. **HIKING** Pinnacles National Monument in California has 71.2 miles of hiking trails. Write this number in two other forms. **Sample answer: seventy-one and two tenths; $(7 \times 10) + (1 \times 1) + (2 \times 0.1)$**

18. **ANALYZE TABLES** In the table at the right, which numbers have their last digit in the thousandths place? Explain your reasoning. Write each of these numbers in expanded form. **7.112, 4.445, 0.889; The thousandths place has three decimal places; $(7 \times 1) + (1 \times 0.1) + (1 \times 0.01) + (2 \times 0.001); (4 \times 1) + (4 \times 0.1) + (4 \times 0.01) + (5 \times 0.001); (8 \times 0.1) + (8 \times 0.01) + (9 \times 0.001)$**

World Records For Smallest Animal	
Animal	Length (cm)
dog	7.112
hamster	4.445
newt	2.54
spider	0.0432
starfish	0.889
toad	2.3876

Source: *Guinness World Records*

Chapter 3 12 *Course 1*

Word Problem Practice (page 13)

NAME _____ DATE _____ PERIOD _____

3-1 Word Problem Practice

Representing Decimals

BASEBALL For Exercises 1–4, use the table.

The table shows lifetime batting averages for leading baseball players.

Lifetime Batting Averages for Leading Players		
Player	Team	Batting Average
Albert Pujols	St. Louis Cardinals	0.331
Derek Jeter	New York Yankees	0.316
Manny Ramirez	Boston Red Sox	0.315
Mike Piazza	San Diego Padres	0.309
Chipper Jones	Atlanta Braves	0.304

1. Write Mike Piazza's batting average in word form. **three hundred nine thousandths**

2. Which digit is in the thousandths place of each player's batting average?
   Pujols: 1; Jeter: 6; Ramirez: 5; Piazza: 9; Jones: 4

3. What is the batting average for the New York Yankees player in expanded form? **$(3 \times 0.1) + (1 \times 0.01) + (6 \times 0.001)$**

4. Which player's average has a 3 in the hundredths place? **Albert Pujols**

5. **BUILDING** When measuring board footage for some exotic woods, a carpenter must use 1.25 for thickness rather than 1 in her calculations. Write 1.25 in expanded form.
   $(1 \times 1) + (2 \times 0.1) + (5 \times 0.01)$

6. **TRAVEL** The summer camp Jason attends is exactly four hundred twenty-three and four tenths of a mile from his home. Write *four hundred twenty-three and four tenths* in standard form.
   423.4

Chapter 3 13 *Course 1*

NAME _____ DATE _____ PERIOD _____

3-2 Lesson Reading Guide
Comparing and Ordering Decimals

Get Ready for the Lesson

Read the introduction at the top of page 142 in your textbook. Write your answers below.

1. Which city has the longest subway system? Explain. **London; Sample answer: 4 is greater than the whole number part of any other number.**

Read the Lesson

For Exercises 2–4, refer to the paragraph above Example 2 on page 143.

2. What are *equivalent decimals*? **decimals that name the same number**

3. What does it mean to annex a zero in a decimal? What happens to the value of the decimal? **To place zeros to the right of the last digit in a decimal; the value does not change.**

4. List three decimals that are equivalent to 0.8. **Sample answer: 0.80, 0.800, 0.8000**

5. Look at Example 2 on page 143. Why is annexing zeros used in ordering decimals? **so that each number will have the same number of decimal places**

6. What does the expression $7.6 < 7.8$ mean? **7.6 is less than 7.8.**

7. What symbol would you use to compare 7.6 and 7.3? Explain. **> ; because 7.6 is greater than 7.3**

Remember What You Learned

8. Explain how using a number line to compare decimals is similar to using a number line to compare whole numbers. **In both cases, the values increase as you move to the right.**

NAME _____ DATE _____ PERIOD _____

3-1 Enrichment
Decimal Letters

The letter A at the right was created by shading part of a hundreds square. There are 26 parts shaded, so the *value* of the letter A is 26 hundredths, or 0.26.

Find the value of each letter.

1. 0.31
2. 0.23
3. 0.26
4. 0.24
5. 0.18

6. 0.27
7. 0.24
8. 0.18
9. 0.18
10. 0.30

11. 0.15
12. 0.34
13. 0.30
14. 0.30
15. 0.23

16. 0.30
17. 0.31
18. 0.28
19. 0.16
20. 0.24

21. 0.20
22. 0.34
23. 0.24
24. 0.21
25. 0.25

26. **CHALLENGE** Use the values of the 26 letters as a set of data. What is the frequency of the value 0.26? Which value is the mode? **2; 0.24**

Answers (Lesson 3-2)

3-2 Study Guide and Intervention

NAME _____ DATE _____ PERIOD _____

Comparing and Ordering Decimals

Example 1 Use > or < to compare 68.563 and 68.5603.

First, line up the decimal points.

Then, starting at the left, find the first place the digits differ. → Compare the digits. → Since 3 > 0, → $3 > 0$ 68.563 > 68.5603

68.563
68.5603

So, 68.563 is greater than 68.5603.

Example 2 Order 4.073, 4.73, 4.0073, and 4 from least to greatest.

First, line up the decimal points.

Annex zeros so that each has the same number of decimal places. → Use place value to compare and order the decimals.

4.073   4.0730
4.73   4.7300
4.0073   4.0073
4   4.0000

| |
| 4.0000 |
| 4.0073 |
| 4.0730 |
| 4.7300 |

The order from least to greatest is 4, 4.0073, 4.073, and 4.73.

Exercises

Use >, <, or = to compare each pair of decimals.

1. 4.08 ● 4.080   =

2. 0.001 ● 0.01   <

3. 23.659 ● 22.659   >

4. 50.031 ● 50.030   >

5. 7 ● 7.0001   <

6. 18.01 ● 18.010   =

Order each set of decimals from least to greatest.

7. 0.006, 0.6, 0.060, 6
   0.006, 0.060, 0.6, 6

8. 456.73, 465.32, 456.37, 456.23
   456.23, 456.37, 456.73, 465.32

Order each set of decimals from greatest to least.

9. 3.01, 3.009, 3.09, 3.0001
   3.09, 3.01, 3.009, 3.0001

10. 45.303, 45.333, 45.03, 45.0003, 45.003
    45.333, 45.303, 45.03, 45.003, 45.0003

Chapter 3   16   Course 1

3-2 Skills Practice

NAME _____ DATE _____ PERIOD _____

Comparing and Ordering Decimals

Use >, <, or = to compare each pair of decimals.

1. 2.4 ● 2.04   >

2. 6.23 ● 6.32   <

3. 0.02 ● 0.020   =

4. 12.05 ● 12.50   <

5. 0.92 ● 0.095   >

6. 39.21 ● 39.021   >

7. 0.849 ● 0.0851   >

8. 12.1 ● 12.10   =

9. 21.967 ● 2.1968   >

10. 0.0128 ● 0.128   <

11. 1.4601 ● 1.460   >

12. 19.08 ● 19.079   >

13. 28.003 ● 28.03   <

14. 0.831 ● 0.0835   >

15. 39.020 ● 39.0200   =

16. 15.6243 ● 15.6234   >

17. 12.0905 ● 12.10   <

18. 56.7 ● 5.67   >

Order each set of decimals from least to greatest.

19. 1.25, 1.52, 1.02, 1.50
    1.02, 1.25, 1.50, 1.52

20. 67.39, 68.004, 67.039, 67.04
    67.039, 67.04, 67.39, 68.004

21. 15.0421, 14.52, 14.521, 15.421
    14.52, 14.521, 15.0421, 15.421

22. 0.0012, 0.0211, 0.0002, 0.0022
    0.0002, 0.0012, 0.0022, 0.0211

Order each set of decimals from greatest to least.

23. 4.99, 4.001, 5.0, 4.01
    5.0, 4.99, 4.01, 4.001

24. 12.0012, 120.012, 12.012, 12.12
    120.012, 12.12, 12.012, 12.0012

25. 3.5, 3.05, 3.55, 3.555
    3.555, 3.55, 3.5, 3.05

26. 45.0, 40.5, 40.09, 49.5
    49.5, 45.0, 40.5, 40.09

Chapter 3   17   Course 1

Answers

Answers (Lesson 3-2)

Word Problem Practice (3-2)

NAME _____ DATE _____ PERIOD _____

3-2 Word Problem Practice
Comparing and Ordering Decimals

MUSIC For Exercises 1–4, use the table.
The table shows the percent of the music market for each type of music.

Music Industry Sales Statistics, 2003	
Type of Music	Percent of Market
Pop	8.9
Country	10.4
Rock	25.2
Rap/Hip-Hop	13.3
R&B	10.6

1. Use > or < to compare the percents for pop and rap/hip-hop. Which is greater? **8.9 < 13.3; 13.3**

2. Use > or < to compare the percents for country and R&B. Which is greater? **10.4 < 10.6; 10.6**

3. If you owned a store that sells CDs, which kind of music would you want to sell, based on the table? Explain. **Sample answer: I would want to sell rock because it has the greatest percent of the market.**

4. Suppose children's songs have 8.05 percent of the market. Is this greater or less than the percent for pop music? Explain. **less; 8.9 > 8.05**

5. CONSTRUCTION Alberto is setting out four boards of lumber. The lengths of the boards are 4.5 feet, 4.52 feet, 4 feet, and 4.505 feet. Order the lengths from longest to shortest. **4.52, 4.505, 4.5, 4**

6. CONSTRUCTION Ella set out a board of pine lumber that was 0.8 feet long and a board of cedar lumber that was 0.80 feet long. Alberto said the cedar board was longer. Is he correct? Explain. **No; 0.8 and 0.80 are equivalent decimals.**

Chapter 3   19   Course 1

Practice (3-2)

NAME _____ DATE _____ PERIOD _____

3-2 Practice
Comparing and Ordering Decimals

Use >, <, or = to compare each pair of decimals.

1. 8.8 ● 8.80   **=**

2. 0.3 ● 3.0   **<**

3. 0.06 ● 0.6   **<**

4. 5.10 ● 5.01   **>**

5. 4.42 ● 4.24   **>**

6. 0.009 ● 0.9   **<**

7. 0.305 ● 0.315   **<**

8. 7.006 ● 7.060   **<**

9. 8.408 ● 8.044   **>**

10. 91.77 ● 91.770   **=**

11. 7.2953 ● 7.2593   **>**

12. 0.0826 ● 0.0286   **>**

Order each set of decimals from least to greatest.

13. 33.6, 34.01, 33.44, 34   **33.44, 33.6, 34, 34.01**

14. 78.203, 78.34, 78.023, 78.23   **78.023, 78.203, 78.23, 78.34**

Order each set of decimals from greatest to least.

15. 8.7, 8.77, 8.07, 8.777   **8.777, 8.77, 8.7, 8.07**

16. 26.0999, 26.199, 25.99, 26.1909   **26.199, 26.1909, 26.0999, 25.99**

17. LIBRARY Books in the library are placed on shelves in order according to their Dewey Decimal numbers. Arrange these numbers in order from least to greatest. **943.6, 943.67, 943.678**

Book Number
943.678
943.6
943.67

18. ANALYZE TABLES The following table shows the amount of money Sonia spent on lunch each day this week. Order the amounts from least to greatest and then find the median amount she spent on lunch. **$4.23, $4.38, $4.39, $4.45, $4.53; $4.39**

Day	Mon.	Tue.	Wed.	Thu.	Fri.
Amount Spent ($)	4.45	4.39	4.23	4.53	4.38

Chapter 3   18   Course 1

Answers (Lesson 3-2)

NAME _____ DATE _____ PERIOD _____

3-2 Enrichment

A Look at Nutrients

The table below gives data about a few of the nutrients in an average serving of some common foods.

Food	Protein (grams)	Fat (grams)	Carbohydrates (grams)	Vitamins (milligrams)			Minerals* (milligrams)			
				B	B-1	B-2	Na	K	Ca	
apple (medium)	0.3	0.5	21.1	8	0.02	0.02	1	159	10	
chocolate bar (1.02 oz)	2.2	9.4	16.5	0	0.02	0.08	29	119	55	
cola (12 fl oz)	0.0	0.0	40.7	0	0.00	0.00	20	7	11	
hamburger (1 medium)	21.8	14.5	0.0	0	0.13	0.15	40	382	6	
orange juice (8 fl oz)	1.7	0.1	26.8	97	0.20	0.05	2	474	22	
peas (1/2 cup)	4.5	0.4	10.8	19.	0.22	0.09	128	137	17	
wheat bread (1 slice)	2.3	1.0	11.3	0	0.11	0.08	129	33	30	
whole milk (8 fl oz)	8.0	8.2	11.4	2	0.09	0.40	120	370	291	

*Na = sodium, K = potassium, Ca = calcium

Use the data in the table to answer each question.

1. Is there more potassium in one apple or in one serving of peas? **apple**

2. Does one serving of milk contain more fat or more carbohydrates? **carbohydrates**

3. Which foods contain less than 0.05 milligram of vitamin B-2? **apple, cola**

4. Which foods contain an amount of carbohydrates between 15 grams and 25 grams? **apple, chocolate bar**

5. Which food contains the least amount of calcium? **hamburger**

6. Which food contains the greatest amount of vitamin B-1? **peas**

7. List the foods in order of their protein content from least to greatest. **cola, apple, orange juice, chocolate bar, wheat bread, peas, whole milk, hamburger**

8. List the foods in order of their fat content from greatest to least. **hamburger, chocolate bar, whole milk, wheat bread, apple, peas, orange juice, cola**

9. Make up two questions about the data in the table. Exchange questions with a classmate. Then answer your classmate's questions. **See students' work.**

NAME _____ DATE _____ PERIOD _____

3-2 TI-73 Activity

Ordering Decimals

Use the TI-73 calculator to sort a set of data that you have entered into a list.

Example   Sort this set of decimals from least to greatest.
5.95, 2.061, 5.6, 4.72, 2.9, 3.213, 4.97, 6.402, 5.6, 5.11, 4.99, 3.4, 2.675, 4.12, 5.006, 3.7, 4.61.

Step 1   Clear all lists.
   [2nd] [MEM] 6 [ENTER]

Step 2   Enter the numbers in list L1. Press ENTER after each number.
   [LIST]

Step 3   Sort the list L1.
   [2nd] [QUIT] [CLEAR]
   [2nd] [STAT] [ENTER]
   [2nd] [STAT] [ENTER] [ENTER]
   [LIST]

The screen shows the list of decimals ordered from least to greatest. The smallest number in the set is 2.061.

Sort the data from least to greatest. Then answer each question.
10.11, 8.61, 9.1, 10.56, 9.067, 8.11, 8.651, 8.7, 9.0, 9.8, 10.65, 8.4, 10.42, 10.019, 9.75, 9.42, 9.6, 10.5, 8.4, 10.001, 8.6, 9.65, 8.41, 8.557, 8.0, 10.9, 10.009, 10.65

1. What is the least number in the set? **8**

2. What is the greatest number in the set? **10.9**

3. What is the fifth number in the ordered list? **8.41**

4. When the bottom line of the calculator's display shows L1(10)=, which number in the list is highlighted? **8.7**

5. Are more numbers in the set greater than 9 or less than 9? **greater than 9**

Lesson 3-2

Answers

Left page

3-3 Lesson Reading Guide

Rounding Decimals

Get Ready for the Lesson

Read the introduction at the top of page 146 in your textbook. Write your answers below.

1. Round each price to the nearest dollar.
   Movie Max: $9; Star Theater: $8; Movie Mania: $6;
   Dollar Theater: $2; Cine-mart: $10

2. How did you decide how to round each number? **Sample answer: Use the rules for rounding whole numbers, but look at the digit in the tenths place to decide whether to round up or not.**

3. Make a conjecture about how to round each cost to the nearest dime.
   Sample answer: Look at the penny and follow the rules for rounding numbers. If it was 5 or higher, go up. If it was lower than 5, round down.

Read the Lesson

For Exercises 4 and 5, see Examples 1 and 3 on pages 146 and 147.

4. In Example 1, what is the underlined digit? What place is it in? Why does the 1 remain the same when the decimal is rounded? **The underlined digit is 1; it is in the ones place; the 1 remains the same because the digit to the right of it is less than 5.**

5. In Example 3, why is the digit in the cents place underlined? Why is it increased by 1 when the decimal is rounded? **Why is it to show that the 8 is the place value to be rounded to; because the digit to the right of the 8 is 5 or greater**

Remember What You Learned

6. Explain how to round a number. Give an example. **Underline the digit to indicate to which place the number is to be rounded. Then look at the digit to the right of the underlined digit. If the digit to the right is 4 or less, the underlined digit remains the same. If the digit to the right is 5 or more, add one to the underlined digit; see students' work.**

Right page

3-3 Study Guide and Intervention

Rounding Decimals

To round a decimal, first underline the digit to be rounded. Then look at the digit to the right of the place being rounded.
- If the digit is 4 or less, the underlined digit remains the same.
- If the digit is 5 or greater, add 1 to the underlined digit.

Example 1   Round 6.58 to the nearest tenth.

Underline the digit to be rounded.	Look at the digit to the right of the underlined digit.	Since the digit to the right is 8, add one to the underlined digit.
6.58	6.58	6.6

To the nearest tenth, 6.58 rounds to 6.6.

Example 2   Round 86.943 to the nearest hundredth.

Underline the digit to be rounded.	Look at the digit to the right of the underlined digit.	Since the digit is 3 and 3 < 5, the digit 4 remains the same.
86.943	86.943	86.94

To the nearest hundredth, 86.943 rounds to 86.94.

Exercises

Round each decimal to the indicated place-value position.

1. 3.21; tenths   **3.2**

2. 2.0505; thousandths   **2.051**

3. 6.5892; hundredths   **6.59**

4. 235.709; hundredths   **235.71**

5. 0.0914; thousandths   **0.091**

6. 34.35; tenths   **34.4**

7. 500.005; hundredths   **500.01**

8. 2.5134; tenths   **2.5**

9. 0.0052; thousandths   **0.005**

10. 0.0052; hundredths   **0.01**

11. 131.1555; thousandths   **131.156**

12. 232.88; tenths   **232.9**

3-3 Practice

Rounding Decimals

Round each decimal to the indicated place-value position.

1. 8.239; tenths **8.2**
2. 3.666; tenths **3.7**
3. 4.47; ones **4**
4. 10.86; ones **11**
5. 3.299; hundredths **3.30**
6. 20.687; hundredths **20.69**
7. 2.3654; thousandths **2.365**
8. 69.0678; thousandths **69.068**
9. 5.58214; hundredths **5.58**
10. 468.09156; thousandths **468.092**
11. $46.49; tens **$50**
12. 1,358.761; tens **1,360**

13. **LANGUAGES** In the United States, about 1.64 million people speak French as their primary language. Round this number to the nearest million. **2 million**

14. **SHOPPING** The price of a pound of cooked shrimp was $3.29. How much was this to the nearest dollar? **$3**

15. **COMPUTERS** Crystal has filled up 13.57 gigabytes of her computer's hard drive. Round this amount to the nearest tenth of a gigabyte. **13.6 GB**

16. **CURRENCY** Recently, one Canadian dollar was equal to 0.835125 U.S. dollars. Round this amount of U.S. dollars to the nearest cent. **$0.84**

CALCULATOR A calculator will often show the results of a calculation with a very long decimal. Round each of the numbers on the calculator displays to the nearest thousandth.

17. | 35.67381216 | **35.674**
18. | 1342.409448 | **1,342.409**
19. | 5.23517.28864 | **0.524**

20. **RACING** The table shows the times for a canoe paddling race at summer camp. Will it help to round these times to the nearest tenth before listing them in order from least to greatest? Explain. **No; if you round the times, some of them will have the same value.**

Canoe Race	
Team	**Time (h)**
Cougars	1.751
Moose	1.824
Jack Rabbits	1.665
Bears	1.739

3-3 Skills Practice

Rounding Decimals

Round each decimal to the indicated place-value position.

1. 54.38; ones **54**
2. 2.671; tenths **2.7**
3. $87.01; tens **$90**
4. 12.0905; tenths **12.1**
5. 441.031; ones **441**
6. 7.892; tenths **7.9**
7. 20.2093; hundredths **20.21**
8. 5.5252; ones **6**
9. 16.01; tens **20**
10. 0.58; tenths **0.6**
11. 0.2859; hundredths **0.29**
12. 145.15455; thousandths **145.155**
13. $10.65; ones **$11**
14. 3.0188; thousandths **3.019**
15. 0.01426; thousandths **0.014**
16. 4.8255; thousandths **4.826**
17. 0.830528; ten-thousandths **0.8305**
18. 143.093541; ten-thousandths **143.0935**
19. 0.0523413; ten-thousandths **0.0523**
20. 137.892; hundredths **137.89**

Answers (Lesson 3-3)

3-3 Enrichment

NAME _____ DATE _____ PERIOD _____

Everybody into the Pool!

Answer each question using the "decimal pool" below.

1. Which decimal when rounded to the nearest hundredth is 0.03?
0.025

2. Which decimal when rounded to the nearest thousandth is 0.003?
0.0029

3. Which two decimals when rounded to the nearest hundredth are 0.02?
0.0209, 0.019

4. Which five decimals when rounded to the nearest tenth are 0.2?
0.185, 0.196, 0.1505, 0.2019, 0.2099

5. Which decimal when rounded to the nearest thousandth is 0.210?
0.2099

6. Which two decimals when rounded to the nearest hundredth are 0.20?
0.196, 0.2019

7. Add to the pool four different decimals that when rounded to the nearest thousandth are 0.301. **Answers will vary.**

8. Add to the pool a three-place decimal that when rounded to the nearest tenth is 1.0. **Answers will vary.**

0.025   0.1505
0.0029
0.196   0.019
0.1099   0.0351
0.2019
0.0209   0.2099
0.185
0.301

9. **CHALLENGE** Suppose that you are rounding decimals to the nearest hundredth. How many three-place decimals round to 0.05? List them. How many four-place decimals do you think round to 0.05? How many four-place decimals round to 0.05?
ten; 0.045, 0.046, 0.047, 0.048, 0.049, 0.050, 0.051, 0.052, 0.053, 0.054; one hundred

---

3-3 Word Problem Practice
Rounding Decimals

NAME _____ DATE _____ PERIOD _____

POPULATION For Exercises 1 and 2, use the table.

The table shows the number of people in the United States per square mile.

U.S. Population	
Year	Number of people per square mile of land area
1970	57.4
1980	64.0
1990	70.3
2000	79.6

1. Round the decimal for the number of people per square mile in 2000 to the nearest tens. Then round it to the nearest ones. **80; 80**

2. Round the decimal for the number of people per square mile in 1970 to the nearest tens. Then round it to the nearest ones. **60; 57**

EVERGLADES For Exercises 3–7, use the following information.
The Everglades National Park gets an average of 59.10 inches of rainfall a year. It had 1.181351 million visitors in 2004, and its budget for 2003 was $13.958 million.

3. How much rain does the Everglades National Park receive each year rounded to the nearest inch? **59 in.**

4. How many visitors did the park have rounded to the nearest tenth of a million? **1.2 million**

5. How many visitors did the park have rounded to the nearest ten-thousandth of a million? **1.1814 million**

6. What is the budget to the nearest million? **$14 million**

7. What is the budget to the nearest hundredth of a million? **$13.96 million**

8. **SNOWBOARDING** Mike, Jake, and Aaron are buying snowboards. Mike is getting his snowboard on sale for $219.49. Jake's costs $279.97. Aaron's costs $234.95. Round each snowboard price to the nearest dollar. **Mike, $219; Jake, $280; Aaron, $235**

Answers (Lesson 3-4)

Page A11 (right)

3-4 Study Guide and Intervention
Estimating Sums and Differences

Estimation Methods

Rounding	Estimate by rounding each decimal to the nearest whole number that is easy for you to add or subtract mentally.
Clustering	Estimate by rounding a group of close numbers to the same number.
Front-End Estimation	Estimate by adding or subtracting the values of the digits in the front place...

Example 1 Estimate 14.07 + 43.22 using front-end estimation.

Add the front digits.   Add the next digits.

$$14.07$$
$$\underline{+43.22}$$
$$5$$

$$14.07$$
$$\underline{+43.22}$$
$$57.00$$ An estimate for 14.07 + 43.22 is 57.

Example 2 Use clustering to estimate $7.62 + $7.89 + $8.01 + $7.99.

To use clustering, round each addend to the same number.

7.62	→ 8.00
7.89	→ 8.00
8.01	→ 8.00
+ 7.99	→ + 8.00
	32.00

An estimate for $7.62 + $7.89 + $8.01 + $7.99 is $32.

Exercises   1-9. Sample answers given.

Estimate using rounding.

1. 59.118 + 17.799
   59 + 18 = 77

2. $45.85 + $6.82
   $46 + $7 = $53

3. 4.65 + 4.44
   5 + 4 = 9

Estimate using clustering.

4. $0.99 + $1.15 + $0.52
   1 + 1 + 1 = 3

5. 3.65 + 4.02 + 3.98
   4 + 4 + 4 = 12

6. 6.87 + 6.97 + 7.39
   7 + 7 + 7 = 21

Estimate using front-end estimation.

7. 81.23
   + 5.51
   81 + 5 = 86

8. 42.06
   + 17.39
   42 + 17 = 59

9. 754.23
   − 23.17
   754 − 23 = 731

Chapter 3   29   Course 1

Page (left)

3-4 Lesson Reading Guide
Estimating Sums and Differences

Get Ready for the Lesson

Read the introduction at the top of page 150 in your textbook. Write your answers below.

1. Round the number of visitors to each park to the nearest million.
   9, 4, 3, 3

2. About how many more people visit the Great Smoky Mountains National Park each year than Yosemite National Park? **about 6 million people**

Read the Lesson

3. Below is a difference estimated by rounding to the nearest tens. Describe in words each step shown.

$$54.3 \rightarrow 50$$
$$\underline{-28.7} \rightarrow \underline{-30}$$
$$20$$

Since 4 < 5, keep 5.
8 > 5, round up.
Subtract 3 from 5 mentally and add 0 since both numbers are rounded to the tens.

4. Below is a difference estimated by using front-end estimation. Describe in words each step shown.

$$68.5$$
$$\underline{-34.9} \quad \rightarrow$$
$$3$$

$$68.5$$
$$\underline{-34.9}$$
$$34.0$$

Subtract the front digits.   Then subtract the next digits.

5. Below is a sum estimated by using clustering. Describe in words each step shown.

$$83.20 \rightarrow 80$$
$$80.14 \rightarrow 80$$
$$79.55 \rightarrow 80$$
$$\underline{+80.09} \rightarrow \underline{+80}$$
$$320$$

Round each addend to the same number.

To find the sum, use mental math: 80 × 4 = 320.

Remember What You Learned

6. Suppose you are shopping for groceries. Which method of estimation would you use to estimate the cost of the groceries and why would you pick this method? You may want to consider accuracy, ease or speed of calculation.
   See students' work.

Chapter 3   28   Course 1

NAME _____ DATE _____ PERIOD _____

3-4 Practice

Estimating Sums and Differences

Estimate using rounding.

1. $68.99 + 22.31$ $70 + 20 = 90$

2. $39.57 + 18.34$ $40 + 20 = 60$

3. $81.25 - 23.16$ $80 - 20 = 60$

4. $21.56 - 19.62$ $22 - 20 = 2$

5. $5.69 + 3.47 + 8.02$ $6 + 3 + 8 = 17$

6. $6.6 + 1.22 + 5.54$ $7 + 1 + 6 = 14$

Estimate using clustering.

7. $\$4.56 + \$4.79 + \$5.21 + \$5.38$
$4 \times \$5 = \$20$

8. $9.7325 + 9.55 + 10.333$
$3 \times 10 = 30$

9. $39.8 + 39.6 + 40.21 + 40.47$
$4 \times 40 = 160$

10. $\$69.72 + \$70.44 + \$70.59 + \$69.56$
$4 \times \$70 = \$280$

Estimate using front-end estimation.

11. $34.87 - 29.12$ **10**

12. $69.45 - 44.8$ **20**

13. $\$78.69 + \$31.49$ **$100**

14. $\$255.32 + \$378.60$ **$500**

15. **SHOPPING** Miriam bought a basketball for $24.99 and basketball shoes for $47.79. About how much did Miriam spend on the ball and shoes?
Sample answer: $25 + $50 = $75

16. **PRECIPITATION** Albuquerque gets an average of 6.35 inches of precipitation a year. Phoenix gets an average of 6.82 inches a year. About how many more inches of precipitation does Phoenix get than Albuquerque using rounding and using front-end estimation?
Rounding: 7 − 6 = 1 in.; Front-end estimation: 6 − 6 = 0 in.

NAME _____ DATE _____ PERIOD _____

3-4 Skills Practice

Estimating Sums and Differences

Estimate using rounding. 1–18. Sample answers given.

1. $2.32 + 2.52$
$2 + 3 = 5$

2. $87.146 - 24.953$
$90 - 20 = 70$

3. $18.93 + 27.45$
$20 + 30 = 50$

4. $\$46.83 + \$18.60$
$\$50 + \$20 = \$70$

5. $\$13.23 - \$2.87$
$\$13 - \$3 = \$10$

6. $43.058 - 15.726$
$40 - 20 = 20$

Estimate using clustering.

7. $59.62 + 60.4 + 60 + 61$
$60 + 60 + 60 + 60 = 240$

8. $\$4.79 + \$5.29 + \$4.99$
$\$5 + \$5 + \$5 = \$15$

9. $8.2 + 7.8 + 7.2 + 7.99$
$8 + 8 + 8 + 8 = 32$

10. $89.04 + 87.55 + 90.101 + 91$
$90 + 90 + 90 + 90 = 360$

11. $15.044 + 14.765 + 14.689$
$15 + 15 + 15 = 45$

12. $\$1.44 + \$0.86 + \$1.00 + \$0.70$
$\$1 + \$1 + \$1 + \$1 = \$4$

Estimate using front-end estimation.

13.
$$\begin{array}{r} 51.62 \\ + \ 6.58 \\ \hline \end{array}$$
$50 + 7 = 57.00$

14.
$$\begin{array}{r} \$233.10 \\ - \ \ 23.62 \\ \hline \end{array}$$
$230 - 20 = \$210.00$

15.
$$\begin{array}{r} 4.57360 \\ - \ 0.58256 \\ \hline \end{array}$$
$4 - 0 = 4.0000$

16.
$$\begin{array}{r} 820.1 \\ + \ \ 3.2 \\ \hline \end{array}$$
$820 + 3 = 823.0$

17. $\$102.34 + \$23.00 + \$32.67$ $\$100 + 20 + 30 = \$150$

18. $652.355 - 52.736$ $650 - 50 = 600$

Answers (Lesson 3-4)

3-4 Word Problem Practice

Estimating Sums and Differences

SPORTS For Exercises 1–3, use the table.

The table shows the percent of annual hospital visits due to sports injuries by males 15 to 19 years of age.

Percent of Male Sports-Related Injuries in the U.S.

Sport	Percent	Sport	Percent
Basketball	25.9	Boxing, Wrestling	4.4
Football	21.3	Exercise	3.8
Baseball/softball	4.1	Bicycling	8.1
Soccer	4.6	Skateboarding	3.6

1. Use clustering to estimate the total number of hospital visits due to injuries in baseball/softball, exercising, skateboarding, and boxing.
   4 + 4 + 4 + 4 = 16, 4 × 4 = 16, or 16 hospital visits

2. Use rounding to estimate how many more visits were due to football injuries than to soccer injuries. **21 − 5 = 16, or 16 more hospital visits**

3. Use front-end estimation to estimate the total number of visits caused by injuries in basketball and skateboarding.
   25 + 3 = 28, or 28 hospital visits

4. **BASKETBALL** Len dribbled a basketball for 43 seconds before Greg got the ball away. Then Greg dribbled the ball for 11.525 seconds before Len got the ball. Use front-end estimation to estimate how many more seconds Len dribbled the ball than Greg. **40 − 10 = 30, 3 − 1 = 2, 30 + 2 = 32, or 32 s**

5. **GARDENING** Kevin is going to plant three new types of vegetables in his garden. The garden store sells packages of tomatillo seeds for $1.67, chili pepper seeds for $0.89, and pumpkin seeds for $2.32. Use rounding to estimate how much Kevin will spend on all three packets of seeds. **$2.00 + $1.00 + $2.00 = $5.00, or $5.00**

6. **TRAVEL** Gloria drove 53.2 miles to her grandmother's home. From her grandmother's home she drove 12.67 miles to her aunt's home. Use front-end estimation to estimate how many miles Gloria drove to get to her aunt's home. Then use rounding to estimate the number of miles again. **50 + 10 = 60, 3 + 2 = 5, 60 + 5 = 65, or 65 mi; 50 + 10 = 60, or 60 mi**

3-4 Enrichment

Horizontal Estimation

Many times an addition problem is given to you in *horizontal form*, with the addends written from left to right. To estimate the sum, you don't have to rewrite the addition vertically in order to line up the decimal points. Just use place value to figure out which digits are most important. Here is an example.

3.11 + 0.4639 + 8.205

The most important digits are in the ones place.

3 + 0 + 8 = 11

The next group of important digits are in the tenths place.

1 tenth + 4 tenths + 2 tenths = 7 tenths

Add to make your estimate: 11 + 7 tenths → about 11.7

Estimate each sum.

1. 7.44 + 0.2193 **about 7.6**
2. 0.4015 + 9.3 + 3.264 **about 12.9**
3. 0.4208 + 0.16 **about 0.58**
4. 0.52 + 0.1 + 0.308 + 0.0294 **about 0.94**
5. 10.2 + 0.519 **about 10.7**
6. 12.004 + 1.5 + 4.32 + 0.1009 **about 17.9**
7. 6.72 + 0.5037 **about 7.2**
8. 0.805 + 1.006 + 0.4 + 2.0305 **about 4.2**
9. 1.208 + 3.1 + 0.04 + 6.143 + 0.3075 **about 10.7**
10. 0.9005 + 5.03 + 7.108 + 0.004 + 10.7 **about 23.7**

This same method works when you need to estimate a sum of much greater numbers. Estimate each sum.

11. 53,129 + 420,916 **about 470,000**
12. 6,048 + 2,137 + 509 **about 8,600**
13. 723 + 4,106 + 4,051 + 318 **about 9,100**
14. 7,095 + 12,402 + 3,114 + 360 **about 22,800**
15. 650,129 + 22,018 + 107,664 + 10,509 **about 780,000**

Answers (Lesson 3-5)

Page 1 (left)

NAME _____ DATE _____ PERIOD _____

3-5 Lesson Reading Guide
Adding and Subtracting Decimals

Get Ready for the Lesson

Read the introduction at the top of page 156 in your textbook. Write your answers below.

1. Estimate the sum of the top two countries. **Sample answer: 50 + 30 = 80**

2. Add the digits in the same place-value position for the top two countries. **850**

3. Compare the estimate with the actual sum. Place the decimal point in the sum. **85.0**

4. Make a conjecture about how to add decimals. **Line up the decimal points. Then add as with whole numbers, and bring down the decimal point.**

Read the Lesson

For Exercises 5–7 look at the paragraph just above Example 1 on page 156 in your textbook.

5. Before you add or subtract decimals, what do you need to do? **Line up the decimal points.**

6. Then, starting on the right, what do you do next? **Add or subtract the digits in each place-value position.**

7. Why do you think the first sentence of that paragraph says "in the same place-value position"? Give an example. **Because sometimes not all place-value positions will have a digit, for example, 23.1 + 5.8. When you add the digits in the tens position, you get 2 + 0 = 2 because there is no digit in the tens position for 5.8.**

8. In Examples 1–5 on pages 156–158 in your textbook, the first step is to estimate the sum or difference. How does the estimate help? **Sample answer: If the actual answer is close to the estimate, this shows that that the actual answer is reasonable.**

Remember What You Learned

9. Tell what steps you would use to evaluate the algebraic expression $x + y$ if $x = 3.4$ and $y = 5.68$. **Sample answer: Replace x with 3.4 and y with 5.68. Estimate the sum by rounding to the nearest ten, which is 3 + 6 = 9. Then line up the decimal points for 3.4 and 5.68. Annex a zero to 3.4. Add as with whole numbers. Compare the actual value with the estimate to see if the answer is reasonable. 3.40 + 5.68 = 9.08 is close to 9, so the answer is reasonable.**

Chapter 3   34   Course 1

Page 2 (right)

NAME _____ DATE _____ PERIOD _____

3-5 Study Guide and Intervention
Adding and Subtracting Decimals

To add or subtract decimals, line up the decimal points then add or subtract digits in the same place-value position. Estimate first so you know if your answer is reasonable.

Example 1 Find the sum of 61.32 + 8.26.

First, estimate the sum using front-end estimation.

$61.32 + 8.26 \rightarrow 61 + 8 = 69$

$$\begin{array}{r} 61.32 \\ + 8.26 \\ \hline 69.58 \end{array}$$

Since the estimate is close, the answer is reasonable.

Example 2 Find 2.65 − 0.2.

Estimate: $2.65 - 0.2 \rightarrow 3 - 0 = 3$

$$\begin{array}{r} 2.65 \\ - 0.20 \\ \hline 2.45 \end{array}$$ Annex a zero.

Since the estimate is close, the answer is reasonable.

Exercises

Find each sum or difference.

1. $\begin{array}{r} 2.3 \\ +4.1 \\ \hline 6.4 \end{array}$

2. $\begin{array}{r} \$13.67 \\ -\ 7.19 \\ \hline \$6.48 \end{array}$

3. $\begin{array}{r} 0.0123 \\ -0.0028 \\ \hline 0.0095 \end{array}$

4. $\begin{array}{r} 132.346 \\ +\ 0.486 \\ \hline 132.832 \end{array}$

5. $\begin{array}{r} 113.7999 \\ +\ 6.2001 \\ \hline 120 \end{array}$

6. $\begin{array}{r} 0.0058 \\ -0.0026 \\ \hline 0.0032 \end{array}$

7. $\begin{array}{r} \$5.63 \\ +\ 4.10 \\ \hline \$9.73 \end{array}$

8. $\begin{array}{r} 5.00921 \\ -4.00013 \\ \hline 1.00908 \end{array}$

9. $0.2 + 5.64 + 9.005$ **14.845**

10. $12.36 - 4.081$ **8.279**

11. $216.8 - 34.055$ **182.745**

12. $4.62 + 3.415 + 2.4$ **10.435**

Chapter 3   35   Course 1

3-5 Skills Practice

Adding and Subtracting Decimals

NAME _____ DATE _____ PERIOD _____

Find each sum or difference.

1.
```
  0.581
+ 11
-------
 11.581
```

2.
```
  4.78
+ 6
-------
 10.78
```

3.
```
  9.6
+ 5.2
------
 14.8
```

4.
```
  7.8
- 4.3
------
  3.5
```

5.
```
 16.79
- 0.51
-------
 16.28
```

6.
```
  1.02
- 0.38
-------
  0.64
```

7.
```
 20.1
+ 3.2
------
 23.3
```

8.
```
  0.86
+ 0.38
-------
  1.24
```

9.
```
  3.84
+ 2.69
-------
  6.53
```

10.
```
  4.17
- 2.58
-------
  1.59
```

11.
```
 47.06
- 38.27
-------
  8.79
```

12.
```
 96.293
- 68.501
--------
 27.792
```

Find each sum or difference.

13. $8.5 + 0.5$ **9.0**

14. $8.3 + 7.9$ **16.2**

15. $5.21 + 4 + 0.2$ **9.41**

16. $3.4 + 3.2 - 6$ **0.6**

17. $0.485 + 9.32$ **9.805**

18. $362 - 145.9$ **216.1**

19. $19.4 - 7.86$ **11.54**

20. $4 + 8.5 + 2$ **14.5**

21. $8.3 + 5.41 + 3.2$ **16.91**

22. **ALGEBRA** Evaluate $b - a$ if $a = 113.04$ and $b = 241.931$. **128.891**

23. **ALGEBRA** Evaluate $x + y$ if $x = 2.057$ and $y = 16.3$. **18.357**

Find the value of each expression.

24. $3.4 - 2 + 6$ **7.4**

25. $16.9 - 2^2$ **12.9**

26. $7 + 2.3 - 5.8$ **3.5**

3-5 Practice

Adding and Subtracting Decimals

NAME _____ DATE _____ PERIOD _____

Find each sum.

1. $5.4 + 6.5$ **11.9**

2. $6.0 + 3.8$ **9.8**

3. $3.65 + 4$ **7.65**

4. $52.47 + 13.21$ **65.68**

5. $91.64 + 19.5$ **111.14**

6. $0.675 + 28$ **28.675**

Find each difference.

7. $7.8 - 4.5$ **3.3**

8. $69 - 12.88$ **56.12**

9. $17.46 - 6.79$ **10.67**

10. $74 - 59.29$ **14.71**

11. $87.31 - 25.09$ **62.22**

12. $19.75 - 12.98$ **6.77**

ALGEBRA Evaluate each expression if $a = 219.6$ and $b = 12.024$.

13. $a - b$ **207.576**

14. $b + a$ **231.624**

15. $a - 13.45 - b$ **194.126**

Find the value of each expression.

16. $4.3 + 6 \times 7$ **46.3**

17. $3^2 - 2.55$ **6.45**

18. $19.7 - 4^2$ **3.7**

19. **BIKE RIDING** The table shows the distances the members of two teams rode their bicycles for charity.

Distances Ridden for Charity	
Lori's Team	**Tati's Team**
Lori 13.8 mi	Tati 13.6 mi
Marcus 11.8 mi	Luis 15.1 mi
Hassan 15.4 mi	

a. How many total miles did Lori's team ride? **41 mi**

b. How many more miles did Lori's team ride than Tati's team? **12.3 mi**

Answers (Lesson 3-5)

NAME _____ DATE _____ PERIOD _____

3-5 Word Problem Practice

Adding and Subtracting Decimals

1. **MICE** The average length of the head and body of a western harvest mouse is 2.9 inches. The average length of the tail is 2.8 inches. First, estimate the total length of the mouse. Then find the actual total length.
6 in.; 5.7 in.

2. **MUSIC** A piano solo on a CD is 5.33 minutes long. A guitar solo is 9.67 minutes long. How much longer is the guitar solo than the piano solo? First estimate the difference. Then find the actual difference.
5 min; 4.34 min

3. **WHALES** The average length of a humpback whale is 13.7 meters. The average length of a killer whale is 6.85 meters. How much longer is the humpback whale than the killer whale?
6.85 m

4. **GARDENING** Alan is connecting three garden hoses to make one longer hose. The green hose is 6.25 feet long, the orange hose is 5.755 feet long, and the black hose is 6.5 feet long. First, estimate the total length. Then find the actual total length.
18 ft; 18.505 ft

5. **ASTRONOMY** Distance in space can be measured in astronomical units, or AU. Jupiter is 5.2 AU from the Sun. Pluto is 39.223 AU from the Sun. How much closer to the Sun is Jupiter than Pluto?
34.023 AU

6. **ALGEBRA** It is x miles from James City to Huntley and y miles from Huntley to Grover. How many miles is it from James City to Grover? To find out, evaluate $x + y$ if $x = 4.23$ and $y = 16.876$. **21.106 mi**

NAME _____ DATE _____ PERIOD _____

3-5 Enrichment

Currency

The currency used in the United States is the US dollar. Each dollar is divided into 100 cents. Most countries have their own currencies. On January 1, 2002, 12 countries in Europe converted to a common monetary unit that is called the *euro*.

The symbol, €, is used to indicate the euro.

The exchange rate between dollars and euros changes every day.

$1.00 is worth about 0.85€.

EXERCISES Add or subtract to solve each problem.

1. Henry bought a pair of shoes for €34.75 and a pair of pants for €21.49. How much money did he spend? **€56.24**

2. Louis receives €10.50 a week for doing his chores. His sister is younger and has fewer chores. She receives €5.25. How much money do Louis and his sister receive together in one week? **€15.75**

3. A gallon of Brand A of vanilla ice cream costs €5.49. A gallon of Brand B vanilla ice cream costs €4.87. How much money will Luca save if he buys Brand A instead of Brand B? **€0.62**

4. Michael passed up a pair of jeans that cost €29.50 and decided to buy a pair that were only €15.86. How much money did he save by buying the less expensive jeans? **€13.64**

5. Jesse's favorite magazine costs €1.75 at the store. If he buys a subscription, each issue is only 0.37€. How much money will Jesse save on each issue if he buys a subscription? **€1.38**

6. Layla wants to buy a CD for €11.99 and a book for €6.29. She has €15.00. How much more money does she need to buy the CD and book? **€3.28**

7. **CHALLENGE** Lynne's lunch came to €4.00. Her drink was €1.50. How much did she spend total? What would be the equivalent dollar amount?
€5.50/$6.47

8. **CHALLENGE** At the grocery store, Jaden purchased a box of cereal for $3.55 and a gallon of milk for $2.89. He gave the cashier $10.00. How much change did he receive? What would be the equivalent euro amount?
$3.56/€3.03

3-5 Scientific Calculator Activity

Adding and Subtracting Decimals

NAME _____ DATE _____ PERIOD _____

A calculator may be helpful in solving equations with decimals.

Example 1 $0.628 + 7.314$

Enter: .628 [+] 7.314 [ENTER =] 7.942

The solution is 7.942.

Example 2 $2.701 + 35 − 24.1$

Enter: 2.701 [+] 35 [−] 24.1 [ENTER =] 13.601

The solution is 13.601.

Add or subtract.

1. $8.2 − 3.57$ **4.63**

2. $86.327 + 0.38$ **86.707**

3. $10.2 − 10.2$ **0**

4. $37 + 68.31$ **105.31**

5. $0.3 + 2.01 + 8.4$ **10.71**

6. $10 − 0.03$ **9.97**

7. $0.084 + 1.4 − 0.72$ **0.764**

8. $3 + 0.4 − 0.001$ **3.399**

9. $800 + 0.080 + 0.0008$ **800.0808**

10. $10 − 0.10 − 0.001 − 0.0001$ **9.8989**

Evaluate each expression if $a = 8.24$, $b = 7.1$, and $c = 0.001$.

11. $a − b$ **1.14**

12. $b + c$ **7.101**

13. $a + b − c$ **15.339**

14. $a − c + b$ **15.339**

15. **CHALLENGE** Evaluate $r^2 − 3s^2$ if $r = 6.25$ and $s = 1.5$. **32.3125**

NAME _____ DATE _____ PERIOD _____

3-6 Lesson Reading Guide

Multiplying Decimals by Whole Numbers

Get Ready for the Lesson

Read the introduction at the top of page 163 in your textbook. Write your answers below.

1. Use the addition problem and the estimate to find $2 \times \$4.92$. **9.84**

2. Write an addition problem, an estimate, and a multiplication problem to find the total over 3 days, 4 days, and 5 days.
   $4.92 + 4.92 + 4.92 = 14.76$; $3 \times 5 = 15$; $3 \times 4.92 = 14.76$; $4.92 + 4.92 + 4.92 + 4.92 = 19.68$; $4.92 + 4.92 + 4.92 + 4.92 + 4.92 = 24.6$
   $5 \times 5 = 25$; $5 \times 4.92 = 24.6$

3. **MAKE A CONJECTURE** about how to find 5.35×4.
   Sample answer: You can find the sum $5.35 + 5.35 + 5.35 + 5.35 +$ $5.35 +$ which is 21.4. So, $4 \times 5.35 = 21.4$.

Read the Lesson

4. When multiplying a whole number and a decimal, it is very important that the decimal point in the product is in the right place. What are two methods for determining the placement of the decimal point in the product? **estimation and counting the number of decimal places in the original decimal**

5. If you place the decimal point in the product of a whole number and a decimal by counting decimal places, how is this done? **count the decimal places in the product from right to left**

6. What does it mean to annex zeros in the product? Why is it sometimes necessary to do this?
   Sample answer: To annex zeros in the product means to add zeros to the left of a number. There must be the same number of decimal places in the product as in the original decimal. If there aren't, you need to add some.

Remember What You Learned

7. Work with a partner. Explain the difference between standard form and scientific notation, and give examples of each. **See students' work.**

NAME _____ DATE _____ PERIOD _____

3-6 Skills Practice
Multiplying Decimals by Whole Numbers

Multiply.

1. $\begin{array}{r} 1.5 \\ \times\ 3 \\ \hline \textbf{4.5} \end{array}$
2. $\begin{array}{r} 0.9 \\ \times\ 6 \\ \hline \textbf{5.4} \end{array}$
3. $\begin{array}{r} 0.45 \\ \times\ 5 \\ \hline \textbf{2.25} \end{array}$
4. $\begin{array}{r} 3.12 \\ \times\ 8 \\ \hline \textbf{24.96} \end{array}$

5. $\begin{array}{r} 3.47 \\ \times\ 5 \\ \hline \textbf{17.35} \end{array}$
6. $\begin{array}{r} 2.08 \\ \times\ 6 \\ \hline \textbf{12.48} \end{array}$
7. $\begin{array}{r} 9.14 \\ \times\ 2 \\ \hline \textbf{18.28} \end{array}$
8. $\begin{array}{r} 0.82 \\ \times\ 9 \\ \hline \textbf{7.38} \end{array}$

9. $\begin{array}{r} 6.3 \\ \times\ 9 \\ \hline \textbf{56.7} \end{array}$
10. $\begin{array}{r} 0.02 \\ \times\ 3 \\ \hline \textbf{0.06} \end{array}$
11. $\begin{array}{r} 9.12 \\ \times\ 4 \\ \hline \textbf{36.48} \end{array}$
12. $\begin{array}{r} 27.3 \\ \times\ 8 \\ \hline \textbf{218.4} \end{array}$

13. $\begin{array}{r} 4.007 \\ \times\ 4 \\ \hline \textbf{16.028} \end{array}$
14. $\begin{array}{r} 3.13 \\ \times\ 3 \\ \hline \textbf{9.39} \end{array}$
15. $\begin{array}{r} 5.02 \\ \times\ 8 \\ \hline \textbf{40.16} \end{array}$
16. $\begin{array}{r} 6.31 \\ \times\ 6 \\ \hline \textbf{37.86} \end{array}$

17. $\begin{array}{r} 8.01 \\ \times\ 5 \\ \hline \textbf{40.05} \end{array}$
18. $\begin{array}{r} 4.325 \\ \times\ 7 \\ \hline \textbf{30.275} \end{array}$
19. $\begin{array}{r} 0.762 \\ \times\ 2 \\ \hline \textbf{1.524} \end{array}$
20. $\begin{array}{r} 0.08 \\ \times\ 8 \\ \hline \textbf{0.64} \end{array}$

21. 6×3.04 **18.24**
22. 2.6×9 **23.4**

23. 13×2.5 **32.5**
24. 1.006×4 **4.024**

25. Evaluate $42.3t$ if $t = 110$. **4,653**

26. Evaluate $231a$ if $a = 3.6$ **831.6**

27. 3.2×10 **32**
28. 4.5×100 **450**
29. $6.2 \times 1,000$ **6,200**

Chapter 3   43   *Course 1*

NAME _____ DATE _____ PERIOD _____

3-6 Study Guide and Intervention
Multiplying Decimals by Whole Numbers

When you multiply a decimal by a whole number, you multiply the numbers as if you were multiplying all whole numbers. Then you use estimation or you count the number of decimal places to decide where to place the decimal point. If there are not enough decimal places in the product, annex zeros to the left.

Example 1 Find 6.25×5.

Method 1 Use estimation.

Round 6.25 to 6.
$6.25 \times 5 \rightarrow 6 \times 5$ or 30

$\begin{array}{r} 1\ 2 \\ 6.25 \\ \times\ 5 \\ \hline 31.25 \end{array}$

Since the estimate is 30 place the decimal point after 31.

Method 2 Count decimal places.

There are two places to the right of the decimal point.

$\begin{array}{r} 6.25 \\ \times\ 5 \\ \hline 31.25 \end{array}$

Count the same number of decimal places from right to left.

Example 2 Find 3×0.0047.

There are four decimal places.

$\begin{array}{r} 2 \\ 0.0047 \\ \times\ 3 \\ \hline 0.0141 \end{array}$

Annex a zero on the left of 141 to make four decimal places.

Example 3 Find $6.3 \times 1,000$.

Method 1 Use paper and pencil.

$\begin{array}{r} 1,000 \\ \times\ 6.3 \\ \hline 3\ 000 \\ 60\ 000 \\ \hline 6,300.0 \end{array}$

Method 2 Use mental math.

Move the decimal point to the right the same number of zeros that are in 1,000 or 3 places.

$6.3 \times 1,000 = 6,300$

Exercises

Multiply.

1. 8.03×3 **24.09**
2. 6×12.6 **75.6**
3. 2×0.012 **0.024**
4. 0.0008×9 **0.0072**

5. 2.32×10 **23.2**
6. 6.8×100 **680**
7. 5.2×1000 **5,200**
8. 1.412×100 **141.2**

Chapter 3   42   *Course 1*

Lesson 3-6

NAME _____ DATE _____ PERIOD _____

3-6 Word Problem Practice

Multiplying Decimals by Whole Numbers

1. **COOKING** Norberto uses three 14.7 oz cans of chicken broth when he makes his delicious tortilla soup. How many total ounces of chicken broth does he use? **44.1 oz**

2. **TIME** Amanda works on a farm out in the hills. It takes her 2.25 hours to drive to town and back. She usually goes to town twice a week to get supplies. How much time does Amanda spend driving if she takes 8 trips to town each month? **18 h**

3. **EXERCISE** The local health club is advertising a special for new members: no initiation fee to join and only $34.50 per month for the first year. If Andy joins the health club for one year, how much will he spend on membership? **$414.00**

4. **BIKING** In order to train for a cross-state biking trip, Julie rides her bike 34.75 miles five times a week. How many total miles does she ride each week? **173.75 mi**

5. **MONEY** David wants to buy 16 bolts from a bin at the hardware store. Each bolt costs $0.03. How much will David pay for the bolts? **$0.48**

6. **INSECTS** One wing of a Royal Moth is 0.75 inch across. How wide is the moth's wingspan when both wings are open? **1.5 in.**

7. **COSTUMES** KJ is making costumes for this year's samba parade. The pattern she is using calls for 2.125 yards of fabric for each costume. How many yards of fabric will she need to make 34 costumes? **72.25 yd**

8. **POOL PASSES** The girl scouts are going to the pool. It will cost them $2.50 per person to go and there are 10 people going. What will the total cost be? **$25**

Chapter 3   45   Course 1

NAME _____ DATE _____ PERIOD _____

3-6 Practice

Multiplying Decimals by Whole Numbers

Multiply.

1. 0.8×6 **4.8**

2. 0.7×4 **2.8**

3. 1.9×5 **9.5**

4. 3.4×9 **30.6**

5. 6×3.4 **20.4**

6. 5.2×9 **46.8**

7. 0.6×6 **3.6**

8. 4×0.8 **3.2**

9. 5×0.05 **0.25**

10. 3×0.029 **0.087**

11. 0.0027×15 **0.0405**

12. 0.0186×92 **1.7112**

ALGEBRA Evaluate each expression.

13. $5.02h$ if $h = 36$ **180.72**

14. $72.33j$ if $j = 3$ **216.99**

15. $21k$ if $k = 24.09$ **505.89**

Multiply.

16. 4.23×100 **423**

17. $3.7 \times 1,000$ **3,700**

18. 2.6×10 **26**

19. $4.2 \times 1,000$ **4,200**

20. 1.23×100 **123**

21. $5.14 \times 1,000$ **5,140**

22. 6.7×10 **67**

23. $7.89 \times 1,000$ **7,890**

24. **SHOPPING** Basketballs sell for $27.99 each at the Super D and for $21.59 each at the Bargain Spot. If the coach buys a dozen basketballs, how much can he save by buying them at the Bargain Spot? Justify your answer. **$76.80; $27.99 × 12 = $335.88, $21.59 × 12 = $259.08, $335.88 − $259.08 = $76.80**

25. **SCHOOL** Jaimie purchases 10 pencils at the school bookstore. They cost $0.30 each. How much did she spend on pencils? **$3.00**

Chapter 3   44   Course 1

Chapter 3   Course 1

3-7 Lesson Reading Guide
Multiplying Decimals

Get Ready for the Lesson

Read the introduction at the top of page 169 in your textbook. **Write your answers below.**

1. The average weight of each block is 2.5 tons. The expression 2.3×2.5 can be used to find the total weight, in millions of tons, of the blocks in the pyramid's base. Estimate the product of 2.3 and 2.5   **Sample answer $2 \times 3 = 6$**

2. Multiply 23 by 25.   **575**

3. **MAKE A CONJECTURE** about how you can use your answers in Exercises 2 and 3 to find the product of 2.3 and 2.5?   **See margin.**

4. What is the total weight of the blocks in the pyramid's base?   **5.75 millions tons**

5. Use your conjecture in Exercise 3 to find 1.7×5.4. Explain each step.   **The estimate is $2 \times 5 = 10$; $17 \times 54 = 918$; $10 \approx 9.18$, so the product of 1.7 and 5.4 is 9.18.**

Read the Lesson

6. When multiplying decimals, what is the relationship between the number of decimal places in each factor and the number of decimal places in the product?   **Sample answer: the number of decimal places in the product is equal to the sum of the decimal places in each factor.**

7. Look at Exercises 1 and 2 above and the answers for these exercises.
   a. How is 25 related to 2.5 tons?   **It is multiplied by 10.**
   b. How is 23 related to 2.3?   **It is multiplied by 10.**
   c. What is the actual weight if 2.3 is multiplied by 2.5?   **5.75 tons**
   d. How is 575 related to the actual weight of the blocks?   **It is multiplied by 100.**

Remember What You Learned

8. In situations where you are multiplying decimals by whole numbers it is easy to think of the calculation as adding the same value multiple times. What does it mean to multiply decimals? Describe some situations where you would need to multiply decimals.   **See students' work.**

Chapter 3   47   *Course 1*

3-6 Enrichment
Multiplying by 10, 100, and 1,000

Can you see a pattern in these multiplications?

$$\begin{array}{ccc}
5.931 & 5.931 & 5.931 \\
\times\ 10 & \times\ 100 & \times\ 1{,}000 \\
\hline
59.310 = 59.31 & 593.100 = 593.1 & 5{,}931.000 = 5{,}931
\end{array}$$

When you multiply a number by 10, 100, or 1,000, the product contains the same digits as the original number. However, the decimal point "moves" according to these rules.

multiply by 10	move to the right one place
multiply by 100	move to the right two places
multiply by 1,000	move to the right three places

Many people use this fact as a mental math strategy.

Find each product mentally.

1. 10×7.402 **74.02**
2. 100×7.402 **740.2**
3. $1{,}000 \times 7.402$ **7,402**
4. 10×0.84 **8.4**
5. $1{,}000 \times 0.5362$ **536.2**
6. 100×3.83 **383**
7. 24.07×10 **240.7**
8. $1.918 \times 1{,}000$ **1,918**
9. 0.075×100 **7.5**
10. 6.1×10 **61**
11. 0.0046×100 **0.46**
12. $0.005 \times 1{,}000$ **5**

Now you can use this mental math strategy to estimate some products. The secret is to recognize when one of the factors is fairly close to 10, 100, or 1,000. An example is shown at the right.

$$\begin{array}{r} 32.83 \\ \times\ 97 \\ \hline \end{array} \qquad 32.83 \xrightarrow{\times\ 100} 3{,}283$$

So, 32.83×97 is about 3,283.

Estimate by rounding one number to 10, 100, or 1,000.

13. 6.57×9 **65.7**
14. 14.32×96 **1,432**
15. $1{,}225 \times 3.548$ **3,548**
16. 0.6214×11.05 **6.214**
17. 98.04×26.331 **2,633.1**
18. 0.0358×9.3145 **0.358**

19. **CHALLENGE** Find the product $1{,}000 \times 16.5$ mentally. How is this different from the other exercises on this page?   **16,500; You must add some zeros to the right of the number.**

Chapter 3   46   *Course 1*

Answers (Lesson 3-7)

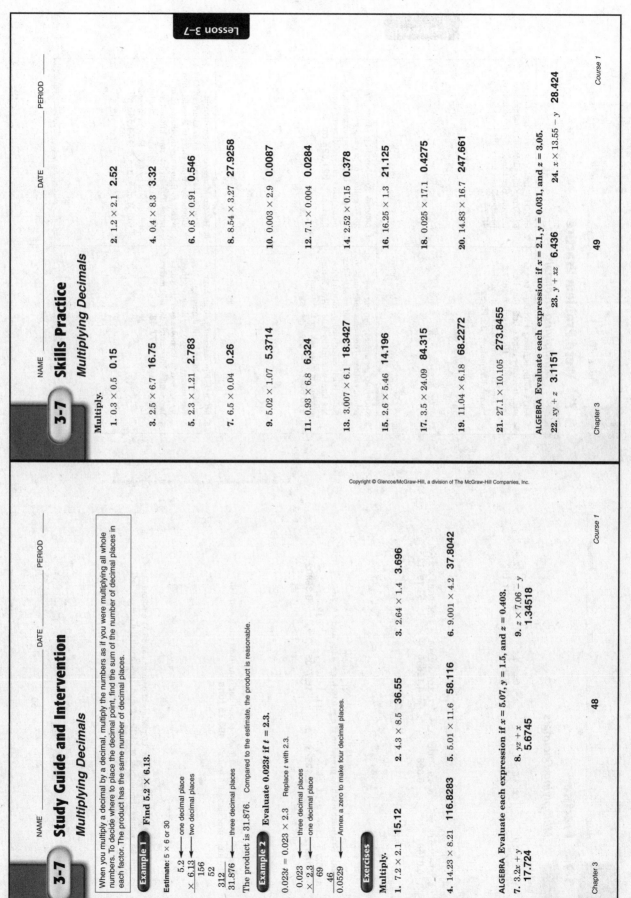

NAME _____ DATE _____ PERIOD _____

3-7 Study Guide and Intervention

Multiplying Decimals

When you multiply a decimal by a decimal, multiply the numbers as if you were multiplying all whole numbers. To decide where to place the decimal point, find the sum of the number of decimal places in each factor. The product has the same number of decimal places.

Example 1 Find 5.2×6.13.

Estimate: 5×6 or 30

$$
\begin{array}{r}
5.2 \\
\times\ 6.13 \\
\hline
156 \\
52 \\
312 \\
\hline
31.876
\end{array}
$$

← one decimal place
← two decimal places

← three decimal places

The product is 31.876.   Compared to the estimate, the product is reasonable.

Example 2 Evaluate $0.023t$ if $t = 2.3$.

$0.023t = 0.023 \times 2.3$ Replace t with 2.3.

$$
\begin{array}{r}
0.023 \\
\times\ 2.3 \\
\hline
69 \\
46 \\
\hline
0.0529
\end{array}
$$

← three decimal places
← one decimal place

← Annex a zero to make four decimal places.

Exercises

Multiply.

1. 7.2×2.1 **15.12**

2. 4.3×8.5 **36.55**

3. 2.64×1.4 **3.696**

4. 14.23×8.21 **116.8283**

5. 5.01×11.6 **58.116**

6. 9.001×4.2 **37.8042**

ALGEBRA Evaluate each expression if $x = 5.07$, $y = 1.5$, and $z = 0.403$.

7. $3.2x + y$
17.724

8. $yz + x$
5.6745

9. $z \times 7.06 - y$
1.34518

Chapter 3   48   Course 1

NAME _____ DATE _____ PERIOD _____

3-7 Skills Practice

Multiplying Decimals

Multiply.

1. 0.3×0.5 **0.15**

2. 1.2×2.1 **2.52**

3. 2.5×6.7 **16.75**

4. 0.4×8.3 **3.32**

5. 2.3×1.21 **2.783**

6. 0.6×0.91 **0.546**

7. 6.5×0.04 **0.26**

8. 8.54×3.27 **27.9258**

9. 5.02×1.07 **5.3714**

10. 0.003×2.9 **0.0087**

11. 0.93×6.8 **6.324**

12. 7.1×0.004 **0.0284**

13. 3.007×6.1 **18.3427**

14. 2.52×0.15 **0.378**

15. 2.6×5.46 **14.196**

16. 16.25×1.3 **21.125**

17. 3.5×24.09 **84.315**

18. 0.025×17.1 **0.4275**

19. 11.04×6.18 **68.2272**

20. 14.83×16.7 **247.661**

21. 27.1×10.105 **273.8455**

ALGEBRA Evaluate each expression if $x = 2.1$, $y = 0.031$, and $z = 3.05$.

22. $xy + z$ **3.1151**

23. $y + xz$ **6.436**

24. $x \times 13.55 - y$ **28.424**

Chapter 3   49   Course 1

Answers (Lesson 3-7)

3-7 Practice

Multiplying Decimals

Multiply.

1. 0.3×0.9
   0.27

2. 2.6×1.7
   4.42

3. 1.09×5.4
   5.886

4. 17.2×12.86
   221.192

5. 0.56×0.03
   0.0168

6. 4.9×0.02
   0.098

7. 2.07×2.008
   4.15656

8. 26.02×2.006
   52.19612

ALGEBRA Evaluate each expression if $r = 0.034$, $s = 4.05$, and $t = 2.6$.

9. $5.027 + 4.68r$
   5.18612

10. $2.9s - 3.7t$
    2.125

11. $4.13s + r$
    16.7605

12. rst
    0.35802

13. **MINING** A mine produces 42.5 tons of coal per hour. How much coal will the mine produce in 9.5 hours? **403.75 tons**

14. **SHOPPING** Ms. Morgan bought 3.5 pounds of bananas at $0.51 a pound and 4.5 pounds of pineapple at $1.19 a pound. How much did she pay for the bananas and pineapple? **$7.14**

3-7 Word Problem Practice

Multiplying Decimals

1. **GIFTS** Colin is filling 4.5 ounce bottles with lavender bubble bath that he made for gifts. He was able to fill 7.5 bottles. How many ounces of bubble bath did he make? **33.75 oz**

2. **GROCERY** Iona's favorite peaches are $2.50 per pound at the local farmers' market. She bought 3.5 pounds of the peaches. How much did she spend? **$8.75**

3. **SHOPPING** Jennifer is buying new school clothes. The items she wants to buy add up to $132.50 before sales tax. Sales tax is calculated by multiplying the total amount by 0.08. What is the amount of sales tax for the items? **$10.60**

4. **DRIVING** Ana bought a van that holds 20.75 gallons of gas and gets an average of 15.5 miles per gallon. How many miles can she expect to go on a full tank? **321.625 mi**

5. **INCOME** Ishi makes $8.50 an hour rolling sushi at Kyoto Japanese Restaurant. His paycheck shows that he worked 20.88 hours over the past two weeks. How much did Ishi make before taxes? **$177.48**

6. **TRAVEL** Manny is on vacation in France. He rented a car to drive 233.3 kilometers from Paris to Brussels and wants to figure out the distance in miles. To convert from kilometers to miles, he needs to multiply the total kilometers by 0.62. How many miles will Manny drive? **144.646 mi**

Answers (Lesson 3-7 and 3-8)

3-7 Enrichment

NAME _____ DATE _____ PERIOD _____

A Logic Puzzle

Here is a puzzle that will help you brush up on your logical thinking skills.

The product 3.3×8.1 is in both the circle and the triangle, but not in the square. Place the product in the diagram at the right.

$$\begin{array}{r} 8.1 \\ \times\ 3.3 \\ \hline 2\ 4\ 3 \\ 24\ 3 \\ \hline 26.73 \end{array}$$

Write 26.73 in the correct region of the diagram.

0.1984

32

1.793

0.0006

20.615

18.447

26.73

0.216

Use the given information to place the product in the diagram above.

1. The product 14.19×1.3 is in both the triangle and the square, but not in the circle.

2. The product 0.08×2.7 is in the triangle, but not in the circle or the square.

3. The product 1.24×0.16 is not in the circle, the square, or the triangle.

4. The product 2.2×0.815 is in both the square and the circle, but not in the triangle.

5. The product 0.02×0.03 is in the circle, but not the triangle or the square.

6. The product 21.7×0.95 is in the circle, the square, and the triangle.

7. The product 2.5×12.8 is in the square, but not the circle or triangle.

8. If you did all the calculations correctly, the sum of all the numbers in the diagram should be a "nice" number. What is the sum? **100**

Chapter 3   52   Course 1

3-8 Lesson Reading Guide

NAME _____ DATE _____ PERIOD _____

Dividing Decimals by Whole Numbers

Get Ready for the Lesson

Complete the Mini Lab at the top of page 173 in your textbook. Write your answers below.

Use base-ten blocks to show each quotient.

1. $3.4 \div 2$ **1.7**

2. $4.2 \div 3$ **1.4**

3. $5.6 \div 4$ **1.4**

Find each whole number quotient.

4. $34 \div 2$ **17**   5. $42 \div 3$ **14**   6. $56 \div 4$ **14**

7. Compare and contrast the quotients in Exercises 1–3 with the quotients in Exercises 4–6. **Sample answer: The digits in the answers are the same, but the problems with the decimal points also have decimal points in the answers the same amount of places from right to left.**

8. MAKE A CONJECTURE Write a rule for dividing a decimal by a whole number. **Sample answer: Divide as a regular number then move the decimal from right to left the number of decimal places in the problem.**

Read the Lesson

9. In the equation $4.8 \div 8 = 0.6$, how can you check to see if the division sentence is true? **Sample answer: multiply the quotient by the divisor. $0.6 \times 8 = 4.8$. Therefore, the division sentence is true.**

10. Where do you place the decimal point in the quotient when dividing by a whole number? **directly above the decimal point in the dividend**

Remember What You Learned

11. Work with a partner. Pretend your partner missed the class that covered this lesson. Explain to your partner the method for knowing where to place the decimal point when you are dividing with decimals. **See students' work.**

Chapter 3   53   Course 1

Answers

Answers (Lesson 3-8)

3-8 Study Guide and Intervention

Dividing Decimals by Whole Numbers

When you divide a decimal by a whole number, place the decimal point in the quotient above the decimal point in the dividend. Then divide as you do with whole numbers.

Example 1 Find 8.73 ÷ 9.

Estimate: 9 ÷ 9 = 1

Place the decimal point directly above the decimal point in the quotient.

Divide as with whole numbers.

```
 0.97
9)8.73
 -0
  87
 -81
   63
  -63
    0
```

8.73 ÷ 9 = 0.97   Compared to the estimate, the quotient is reasonable.

Example 2 Find 8.58 ÷ 12.

Estimate: 10 ÷ 10 = 1

Place the decimal point.

Annex a zero to continue dividing.

```
  0.715
12)8.580
 -84
   18
  -12
    60
   -60
     0
```

8.58 ÷ 12 = 0.715   Compared to the estimate, the quotient is reasonable.

Exercises

Divide.

1. 9.2 ÷ 4   **2.3**
2. 4.5 ÷ 5   **0.9**
3. 8.6 ÷ 2   **4.3**
4. 2.89 ÷ 4   **0.7225**
5. 3.2 ÷ 4   **0.8**
6. 7.2 ÷ 3   **2.4**
7. 7.5 ÷ 5   **1.5**
8. 3.25 ÷ 5   **0.65**

3-8 Skills Practice

Dividing Decimals by Whole Numbers

Divide. Round to the nearest tenth if necessary.

1. 9.6 ÷ 3   **3.2**
2. 5.15 ÷ 5   **1.0**
3. 16.08 ÷ 2   **8.0**
4. 24.64 ÷ 7   **3.5**
5. 132.22 ÷ 11   **12.0**
6. 142.4 ÷ 16   **8.9**
7. 79.2 ÷ 9   **8.8**
8. 47.4 ÷ 15   **3.2**
9. 217.14 ÷ 21   **10.3**
10. 34.65 ÷ 5   **6.9**
11. 20.72 ÷ 8   **2.6**
12. 72.6 ÷ 10   **7.3**
13. 57.48 ÷ 15   **3.8**
14. 264.5 ÷ 25   **10.6**
15. 317.594 ÷ 34   **9.3**
16. 122.32 ÷ 11   **11.1**
17. 42.48 ÷ 18   **2.4**
18. 323.316 ÷ 24   **13.5**

3-8 Practice

Dividing Decimals by Whole Numbers

NAME _____ DATE _____ PERIOD _____

Divide. Round to the nearest tenth if necessary.

1. $25.2 \div 4$
   6.3

2. $147.2 \div 8$
   18.4

3. $5.69 \div 7$
   0.8

4. $13.28 \div 3$
   4.4

5. $22.5 \div 15$
   1.5

6. $65.28 \div 12$
   5.44

7. $243.83 \div 32$
   7.6

8. $654.29 \div 19$
   34.4

9. **WEATHER** What is the average January precipitation in Arches National Park? Round to the nearest hundredth if necessary. **0.48 in.**

January Precipitation in Arches National Park

Year	1997	1998	1999	2000	2001	2002	2003	2004
Precipitation (in.)	1.09	0.013	0.54	0.80	0.89	0.24	0.11	0.16

Source: National Park Service

10. **SHOPPING** A 3-pack of boxes of juice costs $1.09. A 12-pack of boxes costs $4.39. A case of 24 boxes costs $8.79. Which is the best buy? Explain your reasoning.
3-pack; the cost for each box of juice is about $0.36 in the 3-pack, but the cost for each box in both the 12-pack and the 24-pack is about $0.37.

Chapter 3   56   Course 1

3-8 Word Problem Practice

Dividing Decimals by Whole Numbers

NAME _____ DATE _____ PERIOD _____

1. **ENTERTAINMENT** Frank, Gina, Judy, and Connie are splitting their dinner bill. After tip, the total is $30.08. How much does each owe if they split the bill four ways? **$7.52**

2. **FOOD** There are 25 servings in a 12.5 ounce bottle of olive oil. How many ounces are in a serving? **0.5 oz**

3. **RUNNING** Isabella has found that she stays the most fit by running various distances and terrains throughout the week. On Mondays she runs 2.5 miles, on Tuesdays 4.6 miles, on Thursdays 6.75 miles, and on Saturdays 4.8 miles. What is the average distance Isabella runs on each of the days that she runs? Round to the nearest hundredth of a mile. **4.66 mi**

4. **BUSINESS** Katherine spends $1,089.72 each month for rent and supplies to run her hair salon. If she charges $18 for a haircut, how many haircuts must Katherine do to cover her monthly expenses? Round to the nearest whole number. **61 haircuts**

5. **CONSTRUCTION** It took Steve and his construction crew 8 months to build a house. After expenses, he was left with $24,872.67 for himself. On average, how much did Steve make per month? Round to the nearest dollar. **$3,109**

6. **GRADES** Shane wants to figure out what grade he is getting in math. His test scores were 85.6, 78.5, 92.5, 67, and 83.7. What was his average test score? What grade will he receive? **81.46; B**

Grade	Average Score
A	90 – 100
B	80 – 89
C	70 – 79
D	60 – 69
F	50 – 59

Chapter 3   57   Course 1

3-9 Lesson Reading Guide
Dividing by Decimals

Get Ready for the Lesson

Complete the Mini Lab at the top of page 179 in your textbook. Write your answers below.

Use a calculator to find each quotient.

1. Describe a pattern among the division problems and their quotients for each set.
Sample answer: Set A: as the dividend remains the same and the decimal place in the divisor moves to the left, the decimal place in the quotient moves to the right; Set B: as the divisor remains the same and the decimal point in the dividend moves to the left, the decimal point in the divisor moves to the left; Set C: as the decimal point in the dividend and the divisor each move to the left the same number of places, the quotient remains the same.

2. Use the pattern in Set A to find $36 \div 0.0009$ without a calculator. **40,000**

3. Use the pattern in Set B to find $0.0036 \div 9$ without a calculator. **0.0004**

4. Use the pattern in Set C to find $0.0036 \div 0.0009$ without a calculator. **4**

5. How could you find $0.042 \div 0.07$ without a calculator?
Sample answer: Since $42 \div 7$ is 6, you can use the following pattern; $42 \div 7 = 6$; $4.2 \div 0.7 = 6$; $0.42 \div 0.07 = 6$; $0.042 \div 0.07 = 0.6$.

Read the Lesson

6. When dividing decimals, what happens to the decimal point in the divisor and the dividend when you multiply both by the same power of 10?
Sample answer: the decimal point moves to the right by the same number of places in each number. The number of places is the power of ten you multiplied by.

7. Without doing any dividing, describe what you must do to start dividing 0.07 by 1.5.
Sample answer: multiply 0.07 and 1.5 by 10^1, so move the decimal point in each number one place to the right. Annex a 0 in the number 0.7 because 15 does not go into 7.

Remember What You Learned

8. Write a short song or come up with a clever saying that will help you remember that whatever change you make to the decimal point of the divisor you must also make to the decimal point of the dividend. **See students' work.**

3-8 Enrichment
Unit Pricing

The *unit price* of an item is the cost of the item given in terms of one *unit* of the item. The unit might be something that you count, like jars or cans, or it might be a unit of measure, like ounces or pounds. You can find a unit price using this formula.

unit price = cost of item ÷ number of units

For example, you find the unit price of the tuna in the ad at the right by finding the quotient 0.89 ÷ 6. The work is shown below the ad. Rounding the quotient to the nearest cent, the unit price is $0.15 *per ounce*.

```
       TUNA
       89¢
    6 ounce can

      0.148
 6)0.890
    6
    29
    24
    50
    48
     2
```

Find a unit price for each item.

1. 5-pound bag CARROTS $1.29
$0.26 per lb

2. 18-ounce jar PEANUT BUTTER $2.49
$0.14 per oz

3. Grade A Jumbo EGGS Dozen $1.59
$0.13 per egg

Give two different unit prices for each item.

4. Frozen BURRITOS 5-ounce pkg 2 for $1.39
$0.70 per pkg; $0.14 per oz

5. Purr-fect CAT FOOD 3/$1 3-ounce can
$0.33 per can; $0.11 per oz

6. Old Tyme SPAGHETTI SAUCE 12-ounce jars 2/$3
$1.50 per jar; $0.13 per oz

Circle the better buy.

7. Mozarella Cheese 3/$4 10-ounce pkg | Mozarella Cheese 2/$3 18-ounce pkg
18-oz pkg

8. Dee-light Chicken Wings $9.99 5-pound bag | Top Q Chicken Wings $2.29 18-ounce bag
5-lb bag

Answers (Lesson 3-9)

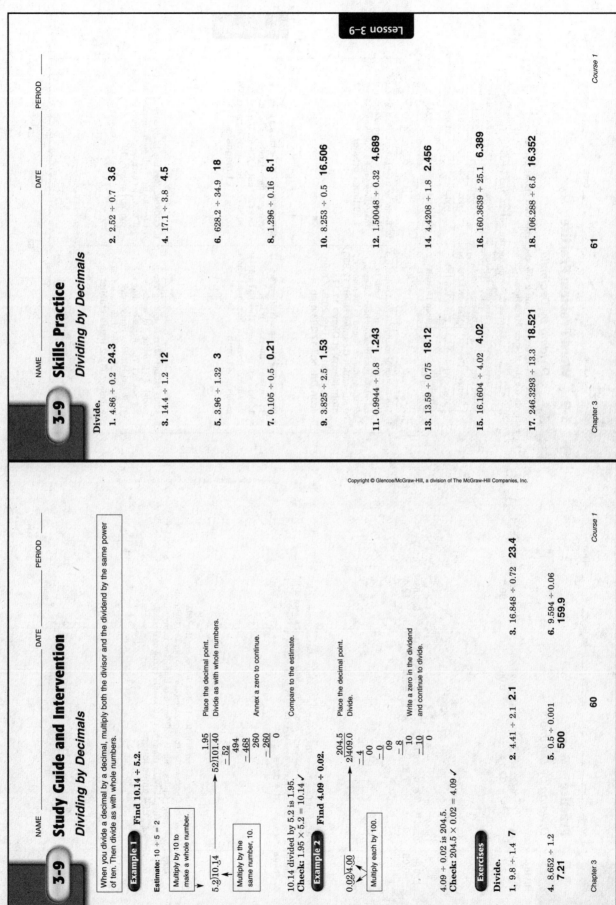

Study Guide and Intervention (Course 1 page)

NAME _____ DATE _____ PERIOD _____

3-9 Study Guide and Intervention

Dividing by Decimals

When you divide a decimal by a decimal, multiply both the divisor and the dividend by the same power of ten. Then divide as with whole numbers.

Example 1 Find 10.14 ÷ 5.2.

Estimate: 10 ÷ 5 = 2

Multiply by 10 to make a whole number.

5.2)10.14 → 52)101.40

Multiply by the same number, 10.

```
      1.95
52)101.40
    -52
     494
    -468
     260
    -260
       0
```

Place the decimal point.
Divide as with whole numbers.

Annex a zero to continue.

Compare to the estimate.

10.14 divided by 5.2 is 1.95.
Check: 1.95 × 5.2 = 10.14 ✓

Example 2 Find 4.09 ÷ 0.02.

0.02)4.09

Multiply each by 100.

```
      204.5
2)409.0
  -4
   00
   -0
    09
    -8
     10
    -10
      0
```

Place the decimal point.
Divide.

Write a zero in the dividend and continue to divide.

4.09 ÷ 0.02 is 204.5.
Check: 204.5 × 0.02 = 4.09 ✓

Exercises

Divide.

1. 9.8 ÷ 1.4 **7**

2. 4.41 ÷ 2.1 **2.1**

3. 16.848 ÷ 0.72 **23.4**

4. 8.652 ÷ 1.2 **7.21**

5. 0.5 ÷ 0.001 **500**

6. 9.594 ÷ 0.06 **159.9**

Skills Practice (Course 1 page)

NAME _____ DATE _____ PERIOD _____

3-9 Skills Practice

Dividing by Decimals

Divide.

1. 4.86 ÷ 0.2 **24.3**

2. 2.52 ÷ 0.7 **3.6**

3. 14.4 ÷ 1.2 **12**

4. 17.1 ÷ 3.8 **4.5**

5. 3.96 ÷ 1.32 **3**

6. 628.2 ÷ 34.9 **18**

7. 0.105 ÷ 0.5 **0.21**

8. 1.296 ÷ 0.16 **8.1**

9. 3.825 ÷ 2.5 **1.53**

10. 8.253 ÷ 0.5 **16.506**

11. 0.9944 ÷ 0.8 **1.243**

12. 1.50048 ÷ 0.32 **4.689**

13. 13.59 ÷ 0.75 **18.12**

14. 4.4208 ÷ 1.8 **2.456**

15. 16.1604 ÷ 4.02 **4.02**

16. 160.3639 ÷ 25.1 **6.389**

17. 246.3293 ÷ 13.3 **18.521**

18. 106.288 ÷ 6.5 **16.352**

Answers (Lesson 3-9)

3-9 Practice

Dividing by Decimals

NAME _____ DATE _____ PERIOD _____

Divide.

1. $12.92 \div 3.4$
3.8

2. $22.47 \div 0.7$
32.1

3. $0.025 \div 0.5$
0.05

4. $7.224 \div 0.08$
90.3

5. $0.855 \div 9.5$
0.09

6. $0.9 \div 0.12$
7.5

7. $3.0084 \div 0.046$
65.4

8. $0.0868 \div 0.007$
12.4

9. **WHALES** After its first day of life, a baby blue whale started growing. It grew 47.075 inches. If the average baby blue whale grows at a rate of 1.5 inches a day, for how many days did the baby whale grow, to the nearest tenth of a day? **31.4 days**

10. **LIZARDS** The two largest lizards in the United States are the Gila Monster and the Chuckwalla. The average Gila Monster is 0.608 meter long. The average Chuckwalla is 0.395 meters long. How many times longer is the Gila Monster than the Chuckwalla to the nearest hundredth? **1.54 times longer**

3-9 Word Problem Practice

Dividing by Decimals

NAME _____ DATE _____ PERIOD _____

MARATHON For Exercises 1 and 2, use the table that shows course records for the Boston Marathon.

Course Records for the Boston Marathon

Division	Record-holder	Year	Time (hours)
Men's Open	Cosmas Ndeti	1994	2.121
Women's Open	Margaret Okayo	2002	2.345
Men's Wheelchair	Ernst Van Dyk	2004	1.305
Women's Wheelchair	Jean Driscoll	1994	1.523

1. The Boston Marathon is 26.2 miles. Use the times shown in the table to calculate the miles per hour for each division winner. Round to the nearest thousandth. **Cosmas Ndeti 12.353 mph; Margaret Okayo 11.173 mph; Ernst Van Dyk 20.077 mph; Jean Driscoll 17.203 mph**

2. To the nearest hundredth, how many times greater was the men's open time than the women's wheelchair time? **1.39 times greater**

3. **DRIVING** The Martinez family drove 48.7 miles to the river. It took them 1.2 hours to get there. How fast did they drive? Round to the nearest whole number. **41 mph**

4. **SHOPPING** Nikki is buying some refrigerator magnets for her friends. Her total bill is $16.80. If magnets are $0.80 each, how many magnets is she buying? **21 magnets**

5. **SCALE MODEL** Matt is making a scale model of a building. The model is 3.4 feet tall. The actual building is 41.48 feet tall. How many times smaller is the model than the actual building? **12.2 times smaller**

6. **COOKING** Yori has 14.25 cups of cupcake batter. If each cupcake uses 0.75 cup of batter, how many cupcakes can Yori make? **19**

Answers (Lesson 3-9 and 3-10)

NAME _____ DATE _____ PERIOD _____

3-10 Study Guide and Intervention

Problem-Solving Investigation: Reasonable Answers

When solving problems, one strategy that is helpful is to *determine reasonable answers*. If you are solving a problem with big numbers, or a problem with information that you are unfamiliar with, it may be helpful to look back at your answer to determine if it is reasonable.

You can use the *determine reasonable answers* strategy, along with the following four-step problem solving plan to solve a problem.

1 **Understand** – Read and get a general understanding of the problem.

2 **Plan** – Make a plan to solve the problem and estimate the solution.

3 **Solve** – Use your plan to solve the problem.

4 **Check** – Check the reasonableness of your solution.

Example **ANIMALS** The average height of a male chimpanzee is 1.2 meters, and the average height of a female chimpanzee is 1.1 meters. What is a reasonable height in feet of a male chimpanzee?

Understand We know the average height in meters of a male chimpanzee.

We need to find a reasonable height in feet.

Plan One meter is very close to one yard. One yard is equal to 3 feet. So, estimate how many feet would be in 1.2 yards.

Solve 1.2 yards would be more than 3 feet, but less than 6 feet.

So, a reasonable average height of a male chimpanzee is about 4 feet.

Check Since 1.2 yd = 3.6 ft, the answer of 4 feet is reasonable.

Exercise

SHOPPING Alexis wants to buy 2 bracelets for $6.95 each, 1 pair of earrings for $4.99, and 2 necklaces for $8.95 each. Does she need $40 or will $35 be more reasonable? Explain. **$40; 2 × 7 + 5 + 2 × 9 = $37**

Chapter 3   65   *Course 1*

NAME _____ DATE _____ PERIOD _____

3-9 Enrichment

It's in the Cards

Below each set of cards, a quotient is given. Use the digits on the cards to form a division sentence with that quotient. Use as many zeros as you need to get the correct number of decimal places. For example, this is how to find a division for the cards at the right.

Cards: 2 3 4   Quotient: 0.0008

You know that 24 ÷ 3 = 8.
So, one division is 0.0024 ÷ 30 = 0.0008. **Sample answers given.**

1. Cards: 4 5 6   Quotient: 0.009
0.054 ÷ 6

2. Cards: 1 2 3   Quotient: 0.04
0.12 ÷ 3

3. Cards: 3 5 7   Quotient: 0.0005
0.0035 ÷ 7

4. Cards: 3 5 7   Quotient: 0.0074
0.037 ÷ 5

5. Cards: 1 2 3   Quotient: 0.0155
0.031 ÷ 2

6. Cards: 1 2 3   Quotient: 0.0025
0.03 ÷ 12

7. Cards: 2 4 8   Quotient: 0.0004
0.0048 ÷ 12

8. Cards: 1 4 6 8   Quotient: 0.03
0.48 ÷ 16

9. Cards: 1 3 5 6   Quotient: 0.005
0.065 ÷ 13

10. Cards: 1 2 3 4   Quotient: 20.65
41.3 ÷ 2

11. Cards: 2 3 4 6   Quotient: 0.0208
0.0624 ÷ 3

12. Cards: 3 4 5 6   Quotient: 0.08
3.6 ÷ 45

13. **CHALLENGE** Use the cards at the right. Write four *different* divisions that have the quotient 0.4.
Cards: 2 4 6
2.4 ÷ 6; 0.24 ÷ 0.6; 0.024 ÷ 0.06; 0.0024 ÷ 0.006

Chapter 3   64   *Course 1*

Answers (Lesson 3-10)

Page 66 (Skills Practice)

3-10 Skills Practice

Problem-Solving Investigation: Reasonable Answers

Solve. Use the determine reasonable answers strategy.

1. **ANIMALS** A male African elephant weighs 6.5 tons. What is a reasonable weight in pounds of a male African elephant? **about 13,000 pounds**

2. **AWARDS** The school auditorium holds 3,600 people. Is it reasonable to offer each of the 627 students five tickets for family and friends to attend the awards ceremony? Explain. **Yes; 3,600 ÷ 5 = 720. Since there are 627 students, there would be enough seats for everyone.**

3. **POPULATION** Use the graph at the right to determine whether 600, 700, or 800 is a reasonable prediction of the population at Midtown Junior High in 2006. **600**

Midtown Junior High Enrollment

4. **FOOTBALL** In 2004, 565,192 people attended the Houston Texans 8 home games. Which is more reasonable for the number of people that attended each game: 60,000, 70,000, or 80,000? **70,000**

Page 67 (Practice)

3-10 Practice

Problem-Solving Investigation: Reasonable Answers

Mixed Problem Solving

Use the determine reasonable answers strategy to solve Exercises 1 and 2.

1. **LIFE EXPECTANCY** Use the graph below to determine whether 80, 85, or 90 years is a reasonable prediction of the life expectancy of a person born in 2020. **80 years**

Life Expectancy at Birth in the U.S.

2. **SNACKS** Paolo is stocking up on after-school snacks. He wants to buy 2 pounds of bananas at $0.79 per pound, 2 cans of mixed nuts at $3.89 a can, and a bottle of apple juice at $1.19 a bottle. Does he need to bring $20 to the store or will $15 be enough? Explain your reasoning.
$15; 2 × $1 + 2 × $4 + $1.20 < $15

Use any strategy to solve Exercises 3–6. Some strategies are shown below.

Problem-Solving Strategies
• Solve a simpler problem.
• Draw a diagram.
• Determine reasonable answers.

3. **CARVINGS** In how many ways can Kwan line up her carvings of a duck, a gull, and a pelican on a shelf? **6 ways**

4. **CARNIVAL** There are 56 students in the sixth grade. Ms. Rockwell's class is sponsoring a carnival at the school. The class has spent $40 on decorations and $10 on publicity. To pay for the expenses, an entrance fee of $0.75 is being considered. Is this a reasonable amount to charge?
Sample answer: No; even if all 56 students came, there would not be enough to cover expenses. 56 × $0.75 = $42 and $42 < $40 + $10

5. **PARKS** The four largest national parks in the United States are in Alaska. The largest is Wrangell-St. Elias at 8.3 million acres. The fourth largest is Katmai at 1.48 million acres. How many times larger is Wrangell-St. Elias than Katmai to the nearest tenth million?
Division; 8.3 ÷ 1.48 is about 5.6, so Wrangell-St. Elias is about 5.6 times larger.

6. **RACING** Hector ran in the city charity race for four years. His times in minutes were: 14.8, 22.3, 26.7, and 31.9. What was his mean time for the four years to the nearest tenth minute?
Addition followed by division; (14.8 + 22.3 + 26.7 + 31.9) ÷ 4 = 23.9 min

NAME _____ DATE _____ PERIOD _____

3-10 Word Problem Practice

Problem-Solving Investigation: Reasonable Answers

1. FOOD Anoki is selling cotton candy at the school carnival. The machine holds enough for 16 cotton candy treats. If he needs to refill the machine every 30 minutes, how many cotton candy treats can he expect to sell in 3 hours? **96**

2. ZOOS The table shows the admission price to a local zoo.

Ticket Prices	
Adult	$7.00
Student	$4.50
Child under 5	$3.00

The Jung family is buying 2 adult tickets, 2 student tickets, and 1 child's ticket. How much will it cost the Jung family for admission to the zoo? **$26.00**

3. AGES Ava's mother is 3 times as old as Ava. Her grandmother is twice as old as Ava's mother. The sum of their three ages is 120. How old is Ava, her mother, and her grandmother? **Ava is 12 years old, her mother is 36 years old, and her grandmother is 72 years old.**

4. PURSES A department store sells three different styles of purses made by a certain designer. Each style comes in navy, black, or pink. How many different purses are available by this designer at the department store? **9 purses**

5. FOOD Keegan stopped by the deli for his mom. If he has $14, does he have enough money to buy 1 pound of turkey, 1 pound of roast beef, and 1 pound of ham? Explain. **Yes; $3 + $6 + $4 = $13, and $0.29 is less than $1.**

Lunch Meat Prices (lb)	
Ham	$3.95
Roast beef	$6.29
Salami	$2.99
Turkey	$2.99

6. PATTERNS Draw the next two figures in the pattern shown below.

Chapter 3 Assessment Answer Key

Quiz 1 (Lessons 3-1 through 3-3)
Page 71

1. six tenths
2. thirty-six hundredths
3. 6.29
4. 4.023
5. >
6. 17.45, 17.451, 18, 18.45
7. 24.0
8. 47.83
9. 2.012
10. 130

Quiz 2 (Lessons 3-4 and 3-5)
Page 71

1. 24.0
2. 47.83
3. 2.012
4. 130
5. $3.00
6. 11.906
7. 23.806

Quiz 3 (Lessons 3-6 and 3-7)
Page 72

1. 7.2
2. 10
3. 15.5
4. 25.2
5. $1.75
6. 7.248
7. 0.1625
8. 11.55 in^2

Quiz 4
(Lesson 3-8 through 3-10)
Page 72

1. 8.3
2. 5.2
3. 3.9
4. 161
5. 120

Mid-Chapter Test
Page 73

1. D
2. H
3. B
4. F
5. A
6. Fill-R-Up station
7. $2.30
8. 13.351, 13, 12.353, 12.35
9. eight and thirty-four thousandths
10. 63.14
11. 30.02
12. 5.34

Chapter 3 Assessment Answer Key

Vocabulary Test
Page 74

1. front-end estimation

2. standard form

3. clustering

4. equivalent decimals

5. expanded form

6. equivalent decimals

7. standard form

8. front-end estimation

9. clustering

10. expanded form

11. Sample answer: numbers that are expressed using a decimal point

12. Sample answer: the point that separates the whole number part of the decimal from the part that is less than one

Form 1
Page 75

1. B

2. F

3. C

4. H

5. C

6. H

7. C

8. G

9. C

10. J

Page 76

11. D

12. H

13. B

14. H

15. D

16. H

17. C

18. J

19. A

20. G

B: $711

Chapter 3 Assessment Answer Key

Form 2A
Page 77

Page 78

Form 2B
Page 79

1. __A__		1. __B__
	11. __B__	
2. __J__	12. __H__	2. __H__
3. __D__	13. __A__	3. __D__
4. __G__		4. __F__
	14. __H__	
5. __D__		5. __B__
	15. __C__	
6. __F__	16. __J__	6. __G__
7. __B__	17. __C__	
	18. __F__	7. __D__
8. __J__	19. __A__	8. __F__
	20. __G__	
9. __C__		9. __B__
10. __H__		10. __F__

Chapter 3 Assessment Answer Key

Copyright © Glencoe/McGraw-Hill, a division of The McGraw-Hill Companies, Inc.

Form 2B *(continued)*
Page 80

11. __C__

12. __J__

13. __D__

14. __F__

15. __B__

16. __H__

17. __B__

18. __J__

19. __A__

20. __G__

B: _____$2.18_____

Form 2C
Page 81

1. seven and twenty-six hundredths

2. fifteen and seven hundred thirty-one thousandths

3. _____47.15_____

4. $(4 \times 10) + (7 \times 1) + (1 \times 0.1) + (5 \times 0.01)$

5. _____<_____

6. _____>_____

7. 15.802, 15.852, 16.1, 16.851

8. _____5.3_____

9. _____13_____

10. _____$0.14_____

11. _____20_____

12. _____$9.00_____

13. _____65_____

14. _____28_____

15. _____10.9_____

16. _____14.83_____

17. _____42.628_____

18. _____4.75 in._____

Page 82

19. _____11.825_____

20. _____30.725_____

21. _____20 in._____

22. _____20.63 in._____

23. _____218.88_____

24. _____42.72_____

25. _____13.0321_____

26. _____564.96_____

27. _____12.5 yd^2_____

28. _____138.71 in^2_____

29. _____1.8_____

30. _____7.8_____

31. _____76_____

32. _____7.05_____

33. _____3.7 oz_____

B: _____$1.86_____

Chapter 3 Assessment Answer Key

Form 2D
Page 83

1. four tenths

2. thirteen and six hundred fifty-one thousandths

3. 32.14

4. $(3 \times 10) + (2 \times 1) + (1 \times 0.1) + (4 \times 0.01)$

5. >

6. <

7. 18.901, 18.951, 19.1, 19.44

8. 7.3

9. 48.80

10. $0.13

11. 17

12. $8.00

13. 52

14. 26

15. 10.7

16. 14.53

17. 38.651

18. 1.75 in.

Page 84

19. 13.935

20. 27.835

21. 12 in.

22. 13.11 in.

23. 42.14

24. 18.72

25. 60.996

26. 587.52

27. 24.5 in^2

28. 130.72 ft^2

29. 7.24

30. 27

31. 8.3

32. 6.01

33. 6.9 oz

B: $1.86

Chapter 3 Assessment Answer Key

Form 3
Page 85

1. twenty-six ten-thousandths
2. two hundred twelve and three hundredths
3. 0.096
4. thirty-four hundredths

5. <
6. >
7. 35.935, 35.1035, 35.036, 3.99

8. 7.0
9. 513
10. $2.40; $32.39

11. 29
12. 3
13. $8.00

14. 33

15. 13.68
16. 1.341

17. The West Coast was closer; $0.052.

18. 1.375 ft

Page 86

19. 4 megabytes

20. 13.1 megabytes

21. 12.508
22. 21.908
23. 17

24. Chi: 5 ft 4 in.; Eli: 5 ft 6.5 in.; Bianca: 5 ft 5 in.; Raul: 5 ft 5.5 in.; Carly: 5 ft 4 in.
25. 13.3
26. 5

27. 9.51
28. 95.76

29. 31.82 m²
30. 44.1 in²

31. 1.35
32. 3

33. 25,750
B: $85.15

Chapter 3 Assessment Answer Key

Extended-Response Test, Page 87
Scoring Rubric

Level	Specific Criteria
4	The student demonstrates a **thorough understanding** of the mathematics concepts and/or procedures embodied in the task. The student has responded correctly to the task, used mathematically sound procedures, and provided clear and complete explanations and interpretations. The response may contain minor flaws that do not detract from the demonstration of a thorough understanding.
3	The student demonstrates an **understanding** of the mathematics concepts and/or procedures embodied in the task. The student's response to the task is essentially correct with the mathematical procedures used and the explanations and interpretations provided demonstrating an essential but less than thorough understanding. The response may contain minor errors that reflect inattentive execution of the mathematical procedures or indications of some misunderstanding of the underlying mathematics concepts and/or procedures.
2	The student has demonstrated only a **partial understanding** of the mathematics concepts and/or procedures embodied in the task. Although the student may have used the correct approach to obtaining a solution or may have provided a correct solution, the student's work lacks an essential understanding of the underlying mathematical concepts. The response contains errors related to misunderstanding important aspects of the task, misuse of mathematical procedures, or faulty interpretations of results.
1	The student has demonstrated a **very limited understanding** of the mathematics concepts and/or procedures embodied in the task. The student's response to the task is incomplete and exhibits many flaws. Although the student has addressed some of the conditions of the task, the student reached an inadequate conclusion and/or provided reasoning that was faulty or incomplete. The response exhibits many errors or may be incomplete.
0	The student has provided a **completely incorrect** solution or uninterpretable response, or no response at all.

Chapter 3 Assessment Answer Key

Extended-Response Test, Page 87
Sample Answers

In addition to the scoring rubric found on page A33, the following sample answers may be used as guidance in evaluating open-ended assessment items.

1. **a.** To put the lengths of the lizards in order, first line up the decimal points of all the numbers. Next annex zeros so that each decimal has the same number of decimal places. Then compare all the decimals by using place value. You must annex two zeros to the number for the gecko, 7, and one zero to the number for the skink, 8.3. The lengths in order from greatest to least are 8.75, 8.3, 8.25, and 7 centimeters.

   b. To round 17.145 to the nearest hundredth, underline the digit to be rounded, which is 4 in the hundredth place. Then look at the digit to the right. Since 5 is 5 or greater, add 1 to the 4. So the rounded decimal is 17.15.

   To find the difference in length between the chuckwalla and the skink, subtract 8.30 from 17.15. The difference is 8.85 centimeters.

2. **a.** To estimate the total rainfall for each season, first line up the decimal points for all numbers for each season. Then annex zeros as needed so that all the decimals have the same number of decimal places. Students' estimates and explanations will depend on which methods they used.

   b. To find the actual total rainfall for each season, you can find the sums using the decimals from part **a** that you lined up and to which you annexed zeros.

   Summer: $1.77 + 0.80 + 2.80 + 3.00 = 8.37$; summer has 8.37 millimeters of rainfall.

   Winter: $4.80 + 4.75 + 6.00 + 8.40 = 23.95$; winter has 23.95 millimeters of rainfall.

   c. To find which season has more total rainfall, you can compare 8.37 and 23.95. Start comparing with the tens digit. Since $2 > 0$, $23.95 > 8.37$. Winter has more total rainfall. To find out how much

more, find the difference: $23.95 - 8.37 = 15.58$. Winter gets 15.58 more millimeters of rainfall than summer.

3. **a.** To find the time volleyball practice got over, take away 15 minutes from 4:45 P.M., the time Taryn got home. Practice got over at 4:30 P.M.

   b. To find the time volleyball started, take an hour and a half away from 4:30 P.M. Volleyball practice started at 3:00 P.M.

   c. To find the time school let out, take away the time Taryn spent doing homework, 30 minutes, from 3:00 P.M. School let out at 2:30 P.M.

4. **a.** Using the estimation method, round 11.25 to 11. 11×6 is 66. Find 6×11.25 as though multiplying whole numbers. The result is 6,750. Since the estimate is 66, the decimal point goes after the 7. The answer is 67.5.

   or

   Using the counting decimal places method, multiply 6 and 11.25 as though they were whole numbers. The result is 6,750. Count the number of places to the right of the decimal point for each number, which is 2. Then count the same number of decimal places from right to left in the product. Place the decimal point here. The answer is 67.5.

   b. Divide $18.57 by $2.

   ```
     9.285
   2)18.570
    -18
     05
    - 4
     17
    -16
     10
    -10
      0
   ```

   They can buy only 9 packs, since they cannot buy a partial pack.

Chapter 3 Assessment Answer Key

Standardized Test Practice

Page 88   **Page 89**

1. (A) (B) ● (D)

2. (F) (G) (H) ●

3. (A) (B) (C) ●

4. (F) (G) (H) ●

5. (A) (B) ● (D)

6. ● (G) (H) (J)

7. (A) ● (C) (D)

8. (F) (G) ● (J)

9. (A) (B) (C) ●

10. (F) (G) (H) ●

11. (A) (B) (C) ●

12. (F) (G) (H) ●

13. (A) (B) (C) ●

14. (F) (G) ● (J)

15. (A) (B) ● (D)

16. (F) (G) ● (J)

17. ● (B) (C) (D)

18. (F) (G) ● (J)

19. (A) (B) ● (D)

20. (F) (G) ● (J)

21. ● (B) (C) (D)

22. (F) (G) ● (J)

(continued on the next page)

Chapter 3 Assessment Answer Key

Standardized Test Practice
Page 90

23. _____2_____

24. _____31_____

25. ___13, 18, 24___

Vera's Weekly Earnings

26.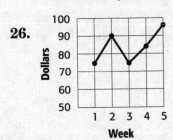

27. _____$84_____

28. Mode; it falls at the
lowest end of the data
set and is not as
representative of the
values.

29. _____<_____

30. _____9.024_____

31a. **7.0 grams**

31b. **No, he's already had 23.6 grams
of saturated fat so far.**

31c. **Sample answer: rounding will
be the most accurate since it
takes into account the decimal
part of each number.**